Literature & Thought

THE BEST OF FRIENDS

Perfection Learning

EDITORIAL DIRECTOR	Julie A. Schumacher
SENIOR EDITOR	Terry Ofner
EDITOR	Rebecca Christian
PERMISSIONS	Laura Pieper
REVIEWERS	Claudia Katz
	Sue Ann Kuby

DESIGN AND PHOTO RESEARCH   William Seabright and Associates,
Wilmette, Illinois

COVER ART   "CIVILIZATION IS A METHOD OF LIVING,
AN ATTITUDE OF EQUAL RESPECT FOR ALL MEN."
—JANE ADAMS   1955   George Giusti

ACKNOWLEDGMENTS
   "Blue Diamond" by Neal Shusterman. First appeared in Tor Books'
From One Experience to Another, edited by Jerry and Helen Weiss.
Reprinted by permission of the author.
   "Building Bridges," copyright © 1998 by Andrea Davis Pinkney from
Stay True: Short Stories For Strong Girls edited by Marilyn Singer.
Reprinted by permission of Scholastic Inc.
   From *Collected Poems* by Langston Hughes. Copyright © 1994 by the
Estate of Langston Hughes. Reprinted by permission of Alfred A. Knopf, Inc.
   "Dawn" from *The Book of Changes* by Tim Wynne-Jones. Copyright ©
1994 by Tim Wynne-Jones. A Groundwood Book/Douglas & McIntyre.
Reprinted by permission of the publisher, Orchard Books (New York), and
Groundwood/Douglas & McIntyre Children's Books.   CONTINUED ON PAGE 144

Copyright © 2000 by Perfection Learning Corporation
1000 North Second Avenue, Logan, Iowa 51546
P.O. Box 500, Logan, Iowa 51546-0500
Tel: 1-800-831-4190 · Fax: 1-712-644-2392

Paperback ISBN: 0-7891-5086-7
Cover Craft ® ISBN: 0-7807-9051-0

WHAT IS THE VALUE OF FRIENDSHIP?

The question above is the *essential question* that you will consider as you read this book. The literature, activities, and organization of the book will lead you to think critically about this question and to develop a deeper understanding of what it means to be a friend and what it means to have a friend.

To help you shape your answer to the broad essential question, you will read and respond to four sections, or clusters. Each cluster addresses a specific question and thinking skill.

CLUSTER ONE What is a friend? **DEFINE**

CLUSTER TWO What would you do for a friend? **ANALYZE**

CLUSTER THREE Friend or enemy? **EVALUATE**

CLUSTER FOUR Thinking on your own **SYNTHESIZE**

Notice that the final cluster asks you to think independently about your answer to the essential question—*What is the value of friendship?*

FOR FRIENDSHIP

For friendship
make a chain that holds,
to be bound to
others, two by two

a walk, a garland,
handed by hands
that cannot move
unless they hold.

Robert Creeley

THE BEST OF FRIENDS

TABLE OF CONTENTS

THE MONSTER AND THE HERMIT: A STUDY IN FRIENDSHIP

A lone: bad. Friend: good."

These four words speak volumes. Almost everybody fears rejection and loneliness, and almost everybody believes that friendship is one of the most precious things in life. We need companionship almost as much as we need food and air. A life of complete isolation would be too horrible to imagine. What wise philosopher managed to summarize such a world of feeling so deftly and pointedly?

These are the words of a man-made monster (played by Boris Karloff) in the classic 1935 movie *The Bride of Frankenstein*. It is a monster movie but in a somewhat unusual sense. Audiences are not so much frightened of Frankenstein's laboratory creation as they are frightened *for* him.

To be sure, the monster is dangerous. But his brutalities are mostly committed in self-defense or by accident. At the very worst, the monster falls prey to a helpless, child-like rage at being misunderstood, unloved, and alone. His greatest yearning is for friendship.

In a famous episode, the monster flees through a forest, escaping his human tormentors. He is drawn to a small cottage by the sweet music of a violin. There he meets an elderly, blind hermit who befriends him. It is a bitter irony, indeed, that only a blind man can truly see into the monster's lonely heart.

The old man teaches the monster the simple joys of food, wine, and music. He even demonstrates that fire, which has always frightened the monster, can be a "friend" that offers comforting warmth. Most importantly, the man begins to teach the creature to speak. And among the monster's first human utterances are those immortal words:

"Alone: bad. Friend: good."

The old man agrees. He has been alone in the forest for too long. "I have prayed many times for God to send me a friend," he says, embracing the creature tearfully.

Alas, the friendship is doomed. A pair of hunters arrive at the hut and recognize the monster. A brief struggle begins, and the hut catches on fire. The monster flees, and the old man is left standing outside his burning home, calling helplessly after his departed friend.

Few scenes in all storytelling have succeeded in saying so much about the nature of friendship. Who among us has not felt like the monster—persecuted, alone, and in desperate need of a friend? And who has not felt overwhelming joy when a friend has appeared at such a moment?

But the scene also explores universal *fears* about friendship, and the hermit's blindness is deeply symbolic. Is friendship, in some sense, always an act of blind faith? Even two people who know each other extremely well don't know *everything* about each other.

Certainly, most of us do not have staples in our foreheads and electrodes in our necks, nor have we committed the monster's crimes. But we do have secrets in our hearts. Is it our duty to reveal all such secrets to a friend? If we do, might it end the friendship? And what should we do when other people, rightly or wrongly, pressure us to give up a friend?

Friendship means trust, and trust means risk. But where there is risk, there is also courage; and where there is friendship, there is greatness of heart and generosity of spirit. It is small wonder that friendships make great drama and great stories, and that those two words harmonize so hauntingly:

"Friend: good."

CONCEPT VOCABULARY

You will find the following terms and definitions useful as you read and discuss the selections in this book.

adversary someone who is on a different side than another

ally someone who is on the same side as another

arch enemy a principal enemy

camaraderie the spirit of friendship

clique a group of people who associate with one another and exclude anyone outside the group

cohort companion; colleague

confidante a friend close enough to be trusted with secrets

elitist a person who feels superior to others; snob

fraternity a feeling of brotherhood among those who share tastes, ideas, or activities; a social organization of male students

gregarious outgoing; sociable

ingratiate use flattery to get on someone's good side

mentor a trusted counselor or guide

nemesis an enemy; a strong opponent

platonic love or friendship that does not include romance

soul mate a person closely suited to another

wallflower a shy person; one who stays on the sidelines at a party or dance

CLUSTER ONE

What Is a Friend?
Thinking Skill DEFINING

DIRK THE PROTECTOR

GARY PAULSEN

For a time in my life I became a street kid. It would be nice to put it another way but what with the drinking at home and the difficulties it caused with my parents I couldn't live in the house.

I made a place for myself in the basement by the furnace and hunted and fished in the woods around the small town. But I had other needs as well—clothes, food, school supplies—and they required money.

I was not afraid of work and spent most of my summers working on farms for two, three and finally five dollars a day. This gave me enough for school clothes, though never for enough clothes or the right kind; I was never cool or in. But during the school year I couldn't leave town to work the farms. I looked for odd jobs but most of them were taken by the boys who stayed in town through the summer. All the conventional jobs like working in the markets or at the drugstore were gone and all I could find was setting pins in the small bowling alley over the Four Clover Bar.

It had just six alleys and they were busy all the time—there were leagues each night from seven to eleven—but the pay for truly brutal work was only seven cents a line. There weren't many boys willing to do the work but with so few alleys, it was still very hard to earn much money. A dollar a night was not uncommon and three was outstanding.

To make up the difference I started selling newspapers in the bars at night. This kept me up and out late, and I often came home at midnight. But it added to my income so that I could stay above water.

Unfortunately it also put me in the streets at a time when there was what might be called a rough element. There weren't gangs then, not exactly, but there were groups of boys who more or less hung out together and got into trouble. They were the forerunners of the gangs we have now, but with some singular differences. They did not have firearms—but many carried switchblade knives.

These groups were predatory, and they hunted the streets at night.

I became their favorite target in this dark world. Had the town been larger I might have hidden from them, or found different routes. But there was only a small uptown section and it was impossible for me to avoid them. They would catch me walking a dark street and surround me and with threats and blows steal what money I had earned that night.

I tried fighting back but there were usually several of them. I couldn't win. Because I was from "the wrong side of the tracks" I didn't think I could go to the authorities. It all seemed hopeless.

And then I met Dirk.

The bowling alley was on a second floor and had a window in back of the pit area. When all the lanes were going, the heat from the pin lights made the temperature close to a hundred degrees. Outside the window a ladder led to the roof. One fall evening, instead of leaving work through the front door, I made my way out the window and up the ladder onto the roof. I hoped to find a new way home to escape the boys who waited for me. That night one of the league bowlers had bowled a perfect game—300—and in celebration had bought the pit boys hamburgers and Cokes. I had put the burger and Coke in a bag to take back to my basement. The bag had grease stains and smelled of toasted buns, and my mouth watered as I moved from the roof of the bowling alley to the flat roof over the hardware store, then down a fire escape that led to a dark alcove off an alley.

There was a black space beneath the stairs and as I reached the bottom and my foot hit the ground I heard a low growl. It was not loud, more a rumble that seemed to come from the earth and so full of menace that it stopped me cold, my foot frozen in midair.

I raised my foot and the growl stopped.

I lowered my foot and the growl came again. My foot went up and it stopped.

I stood there, trying to peer through the steps of the fire escape. For a time I couldn't see more than a dark shape crouched back in the gloom. There was a head and a back, and as my eyes became accustomed to the dark I could see that it had scraggly, scruffy hair and two eyes that glowed yellow.

We were at an impasse. I didn't want to climb up the ladder again but if I stepped to the ground it seemed likely I would be bitten. I hung there for a full minute before I thought of the hamburger. I could use it as a decoy and get away.

The problem was the hamburger smelled *so* good and I was *so* hungry.

I decided to give the beast under the stairs half a burger. I opened the sack, unwrapped the tinfoil and threw half the sandwich under the steps, then jumped down and ran for the end of the alley. I was just getting my stride, legs and arms pumping, pulling air with a heaving chest, when I rounded the corner and ran smack into the latest group of boys who were terrorizing me.

There were four of them, led by a thug—he and two of the others would ultimately land in prison—named, absurdly, "Happy" Santun.

Happy was built like an upright freezer and had just about half the intelligence but this time it was easy. I'd run right into him.

"Well—lookit here. He came to *us* this time . . ."

Over the months I had developed a policy of flee or die—run as fast as I could to avoid the pain, and to hang on to my hard-earned money. Sometimes it worked, but most often they caught me.

This time, they already had me. I could have handed over the money, taken a few hits and been done with it, but something in me snapped and I hit Happy in the face with every ounce of strength in my puny body.

He brushed off the blow easily and I went down in a welter of blows and kicks from all four of them. I curled into a ball to protect what I could. I'd done this before, many times, and knew that they would stop sometime—although I suspected that because I'd hit Happy it might take longer than usual for them to get bored hitting me.

Instead there was some commotion that I didn't understand and the kicks stopped coming. There was a snarling growl that seemed to come from the bowels of the earth, followed by the sound of ripping cloth, screams, and then the fading slap of footsteps running away.

For another minute I remained curled up, then opened my eyes to find that I was alone.

But when I rolled over I saw the dog.

It was the one that had been beneath the stairs. Brindled,[1] patches of hair gone, one ear folded over and the other standing straight and

---

1 **brindled:** having dark streaks on a grey or tawny background

notched from fighting. He didn't seem to be any particular breed. Just big and rangy, right on the edge of ugly, though I would come to think of him as beautiful. He was Airedale crossed with hound crossed with alligator.

Alley dog. Big, tough, mean alley dog. As I watched he spit cloth—it looked like blue jeans—out of his mouth.

"You bit Happy, and sent them running?" I asked.

He growled, and I wasn't sure if it was with menace, but he didn't bare his teeth and didn't seem to want to attack me. Indeed, he had saved me.

"Why?" I asked. "What did I do to deserve . . . oh, the hamburger."

I swear, he pointedly looked at the bag with the second half of hamburger in it.

"You want more?"

He kept staring at the bag and I thought, *Well, he sure as heck deserves it.* I opened the sack and gave him the rest of it, which disappeared down his throat as if a hole had opened into the universe.

He looked at the bag.

"That's it," I said, brushing my hands together. "The whole thing."

A low growl.

"You can rip my head off—there still isn't any more hamburger." I removed the Coke and handed him the bag, which he took, held on the ground with one foot and deftly ripped open with his teeth.

"See? Nothing." I was up by this time and I started to walk away. "Thanks for the help . . ."

He followed me. Not close, perhaps eight feet back, but matching my speed. It was now nearly midnight and I was tired and sore from setting pins and from the kicks that had landed on my back and sides.

"I don't have anything to eat at home but crackers and peanut butter and jelly," I told him. I kept some food in the basement of the apartment building, where I slept near the furnace.

He kept following and, truth be known, I didn't mind. I was still half scared of him but the memory of him spitting out bits of Happy's pants and the sound of the boys running off made me smile. When I arrived at the apartment house I held the main door open and he walked right in. I opened the basement door and he followed me down the steps into the furnace room.

I turned the light on and could see that my earlier judgment had been correct. He was scarred from fighting, skinny and flat sided with patches of hair gone. His nails were worn down from scratching concrete.

"Dirk," I said. "I'll call you Dirk." I had been trying to read a detective novel and there was a tough guy in it named Dirk. "You look like somebody named Dirk."

And so we sat that first night. I had two boxes of Ritz crackers I'd hustled somewhere, a jar of peanut butter and another one of grape jelly, and a knife from the kitchen upstairs. I would smear a cracker, hand it to him—he took each one with great care and gentleness—and then eat one myself. We did this, back and forth, until both boxes were empty and my stomach was bulging; then I fell asleep on the old outdoor lounge I used for furniture.

The next day was a school day. I woke up and found Dirk under the basement stairs, watching me. When I opened the door he trotted up the steps and outside—growling at me as he went past—and I started off to school.

He followed me at a distance, then stopped across the street when I went into the front of the school building. I thought I'd probably never see him again.

But he was waiting when I came out that afternoon, sitting across the street by a mailbox. I walked up to him.

"Hi, Dirk." I thought of petting him but when I reached a hand out he growled. "All right—no touching."

I turned and made my way toward the bowling alley. It was Friday and sometimes on Friday afternoon there were people who wanted to bowl early and I could pick up a dollar or two setting pins.

Dirk followed about four feet back—closer than before—and as I made my way along Second Street and came around the corner by Ecker's Drugstore I ran into Happy. He had only two of his cohorts with him and I don't think they had intended to do me harm, but I surprised them and Happy took a swing at me.

Dirk took him right in the middle. I mean bit him in the center of his stomach, hard, before Happy's fist could get to me. Happy screamed and doubled over and Dirk went around and ripped into his rear and kept tearing at it even as Happy and his two companions fled down the street.

It was absolutely great. Maybe one of the great moments of my life.

I had a bodyguard.

It was as close to having a live nuclear weapon as you can get. I cannot say we became friends. I touched him only once, when he wasn't looking—I petted him on the head and received a growl and a lifted lip for it. But we became constant companions. Dirk moved into the basement with me, and I gave him a hamburger every day and hustled up dog food for him and many nights we sat down there eating Ritz crackers and he watched me working on stick model airplanes.

He followed me to school, waited for me, followed me to the bowling alley, waited for me. He was with me everywhere I went, always back three or four feet, always with a soft growl, and to my great satisfaction every time he saw Happy—*every* time—Dirk would try to remove some part of his body with as much violence as possible.

He caused Happy and his mob to change their habits. They not only stopped hunting me but went out of their way to avoid me, or more specifically, Dirk. In fact after that winter and spring they never bothered me again, even after Dirk was gone.

Dirk came to a wonderful end. I always thought of him as a street dog—surely nobody owned him—and in the summer when I was hired to work on a farm four miles east of town I took him with me. We walked all the way out to the farm, Dirk four feet in back of me, and he would trot along beside the tractor when I plowed, now and then chasing the hundreds of seagulls that came for the worms the plow turned up.

The farmer, whose name was Olaf, was a bachelor and did not have a dog. I looked over once to see Dirk sitting next to Olaf while we ate some sandwiches and when Olaf reached out to pet him Dirk actually—this was the first time I'd seen it—wagged his tail.

He'd found a home.

I worked the whole summer there and when it came time to leave, Dirk remained sitting in the yard as I walked down the driveway. The next summer I had bought an old Dodge for twenty-five dollars and I drove out to Olaf's to say hello and saw Dirk out in a field with perhaps two hundred sheep. He wasn't herding them, or chasing them, but was just standing there, watching the flock.

"You have him with the sheep?" I asked Olaf.

He nodded. "Last year I lost forty-three to coyotes," he said. "This year not a one. He likes to guard things, doesn't he?"

I thought of Dirk chasing Happy down the street, and later spitting out bits of his pants, and I smiled. "Yeah, he sure does." ∾

FOR HEIDI WITH BLUE HAIR

FLEUR ADCOCK

When you dyed your hair blue
(or, at least, ultramarine
for the clipped sides, with a crest
of jet-black spikes on top)
you were sent home from school

because, as the headmistress put it,
although dyed hair was not
specifically forbidden, yours
was, apart from anything else,
not done in the school colours.

Tears in the kitchen, telephone-calls
to school from your freedom-loving father:
'She's not a punk in her behaviour;
it's just a style.' (You wiped your eyes,
also not in a school colour.)

'She discussed it with me first —
we checked the rules.' 'And anyway, Dad,
it cost twenty-five dollars.
Tell them it won't wash out—not even if I
wanted to try.'

It would have been unfair to mention
your mother's death, but that
shimmered behind the arguments.
The school had nothing else against you;
the teachers twittered and gave in.

Next day your black friend had hers done
in grey, white and flaxen yellow—
the school colours precisely:
an act of solidarity, a witty
tease. The battle was already won.

JOE KING

BAILEY WHITE

When I was a little girl, I used to pal around with an old horse trainer named Joe King. He worked for our rich neighbors down the road, the Sedgwicks, who lived in Cleveland and came to their Georgia home only in winter for the climate and the hunting.

In the fall and winter Joe King had to work hard. Everything had to be kept just so. There were the horses, the mules that pulled the hunting buggies, the harnesses, the barns, and the kennels full of bird dogs so high-strung and alert that they looked like they were made out of springs wound up too tight.

In October ryegrass seed would be sowed on the lawns and up and down the drive to the big house.[1] After just one rain the seed would sprout, and the startling green of the ryegrass would look like a bright scar against the natural colors of fall—gray and brown and the pinkish tan of broomsedge.[2]

The big house would be thrown open, silver would be polished, Oriental rugs would be dragged into the yard to air, and Joe King would trim up the horses and grease the axles of the hunting buggies. Millet and benne seed would be planted in clearings in the woods as bait for doves and quail. Everything would be put in order.

There would be a few days of cold. The trees would lose their leaves. Then one frosty morning the ground would be covered with fat, sluggish

---

1 **big house:** main house on a property that also has smaller outbuildings

2 **broomsedge:** a type of grass that grows in the southeastern United States

robins. "Winter's coming," Joe King would tell me. After that I wouldn't see him for a long time.

But in the spring and summer, when the Sedgwicks had gone back to Cleveland, everything would relax. The big house would be closed up, and the horses would loll around with one hind foot cocked up, swatting flies with their tails. Even the bird dogs would relax in their doghouses with their feet flopping over the edge. Almost every day Joe King would drive into our yard, I would climb into his rattly, powdery blue pickup truck, and he would take me down to the Sedgwicks' place. There would be Tony, "my" horse, a horse so old he had been named for a contemporary of his from the silent movies. Tony would hang his head over my shoulder and flop his old bristly lips against my neck. "He's glad to see you," Joe King would say.

I would scramble up onto Tony's high, narrow back, and Joe King would swing up on his horse, a flighty, prancing, light-footed mare named Princess, imported from Kentucky, and we would set out. Tony would fix his bleary gaze on a point way down the road and get ready to move. He seemed to owe his powers of locomotion not to any current process of thought but to some dim memory of walking that would come drifting back to him across the years. The Kentucky princess would dance and prance around him, flicking her little feet out and darting her head up and down. Before we'd gone a mile, she'd be dripping sweat and froth. But Tony would still be staring down the road, plodding along with his stultifyingly economical gait, cool and dry.

For entertainment, and to soothe the mare, Joe King and I would sing songs to each other. My favorite of his went like this:

William Matrimatoes
He's a good fisherman
Catches hens
Put 'em in pens
Wire bright
Clock fell down
Little mice run around
Old dirty dishrag
You spell out and go.

I would sing him songs I had learned out of my *Little Golden Songbook* at school. I liked one about robins. It told about a little boy seeing a robin tap-tap-tapping on the windowpane and how he knew then that spring had come.

"Humph," said Joe King. "Something wrong with that song. Sure is something wrong with that song." We couldn't figure it out. Still, it had a nice tune, and I liked the tap-tap-tapping part in the chorus.

Then one fall, just before the Sedgwicks came, Tony began to die. Joe King came and got me and drove me down there. Tony was standing in the pasture under a big oak tree. He was gazing at something far away, just like he did when he walked down the road, only now he wouldn't move. He didn't seem to be hurting anywhere. He just acted like slowness had finally overtaken him. When I put my hand under his mouth, he flapped his lips one time and blew out a little puff of air.

He stood there for four days, watching his long, peaceful life pass in review. Then, one morning he was dead. They brought out a tractor and put a chain around his neck and dragged him away. The little Kentucky mare went wild. She danced around and around the pasture with her head high and the whites of her eyes showing and her tail flying like a banner. Joe King caught her finally and held her still. He hugged her with one arm and me with the other. He hugged rough, just like you would hug a horse, with my head clamped against his side.

The mare stood up high on her feet and stared down the road where they had dragged Tony. She was trembling and shaking. Then she lifted her head and gave out a high, blowing whistle. It was almost like a cry. Joe King slapped her on the shoulder. "He's gone," Joe King said. "He ain't never coming back." The horse whistled again, and Joe King gave her another comforting clap. "He's dead and gone, and you ain't never gon' see him no more."

Then, that very winter, Joe King died. My mother dressed me all up in white, and we went to the funeral. I had never been to a funeral before, and I was mesmerized by the spectacle of it. There was loud singing and hollering, and Joe King's sister threw herself into the coffin with him and had to be pulled away. When I looked at him, the fact that he was wearing clothes I'd never seen before seemed more surprising than the fact that he was dead.

Spring came and the Sedgwicks went back to Cleveland. But Joe King didn't drive up into our yard in his powdery blue pickup truck smelling like horses and saddles and axle grease and Prince Albert. That's when I really missed him for the first time.

And I still miss him. Every year, when the robins have flown back up north and the trees are showing their first green, I think about Joe King. I remember the elegant grieving of the Kentucky mare, and the eerie, high, blowing whistle she gave. That's how I would like to mourn. But I don't have that much style. Instead, I take a little walk in the spring sunshine, and I say to myself:

William Matrimatoes
He's a good fisherman
Catches hens
Put 'em in pens
Wire bright
Clock fell down
Little mice run around
Old dirty dishrag
You spell out and go. ❧

A FILLY
1969
Lucian Freud

Dawn

Tim Wynne-Jones

Barnsey met Dawn on the night bus to North Bay. His mother put him on at Ottawa, just after supper. His parents owned a store and the Christmas season was frantic, so for the third year in a row, Barnsey was going up to Grandma Barrymore's and his parents would follow Christmas day. He had cousins in North Bay,[1] so it was fine with Barnsey, as long as he didn't have to sit beside someone weird the whole way.

"What if I have to sit beside someone weird the whole way?" he asked his mother in the bus terminal. She cast him a warning look. A let's-not-make-a-scene look. Barnsey figured she was in a hurry to get back to the store.

"You are thirteen, Matthew," she said. There was an edge in her voice that hadn't been there before. "Has anything bad happened to you yet?"

Barnsey was picking out a couple of magazines for the trip: *Guitar World* and *Sports Illustrated*. "I didn't say anything *bad* was going to happen. If anything bad happens, I make a racket and the bus driver deals with it. I know all that. I'm just talking about someone weird."

"For instance?" said his mother.

"Someone who smells. Someone really, really fat who spills over onto my seat. Someone who wants to talk about her liver operation."

His mother paid for the magazines and threw in a Kit Kat, too. Barnsey didn't remind her that she'd already bought him a Kit Kat, and

---

1 **North Bay:** city in SE Ontario, Canada

let him buy a Coke, chips, and some gum. And this was apart from the healthy stuff she had already packed at home. She was usually pretty strict about junk food.

"I just asked," said Barnsey.

"Come on," said his mother, giving his shoulder a bit of a squeeze. "Or the only *weird* person you're going to be sitting beside is your mother on the way back to the store."

Barnsey didn't bother to ask if that was an option. His parents put a lot of stock in planning. They didn't put much stock in spontaneity.

"What if I end up in Thunder Bay by mistake?"

His mother put her arm around him. He was almost as tall as she was now. "Matthew," she said in her let's-be-rational voice. "That would require quite a mistake on your part. But, if it were to happen, you have a good head on your shoulders *and* your own bank card."

His mother almost looked as if she was going to say something about how they had always encouraged him to be independent, but luckily she noticed it was boarding time.

They were at Bay 6, and his mother suddenly gave him a very uncharacteristic hug. A bear hug. They weren't a hugging kind of family. She looked him in the eyes.

"Matthew," she said. "It's not so long. Remember that."

"I know," said Barnsey. But he wasn't sure if his mother meant the trip or the time before he'd see her again. He couldn't tell.

They moved through the line toward the driver, who was taking tickets at the door of the bus.

"Don't do the thing with the money," Barnsey whispered to his mother.

"Why not?" she said. Barnsey didn't answer. "It's just good business. And besides, young man, I'll do what I please."

And she did. As Barnsey gave the driver his ticket, Barnsey's mother ripped a twenty-dollar bill in half ceremoniously in front of the driver's face. She gave half the bill to Barnsey, who shoved it quickly in his pocket.

"Here, my good man," said his mother to the bus driver in her store voice. "My son will give you the other half upon arrival in North Bay. Merry Christmas."

The driver thanked her. But he gave Barnsey a secret kind of cockeyed look, as if to say, Does she pull this kind of stunt all the time?

Then Barnsey was on board the bus, and there was Dawn.

There was no other seat. His mother had once told him that if there weren't any seats left, the bus company would have to get a bus just for him. That was the way they did business. So Barnsey shuffled up and down the bus a couple of times even after he'd put his bag up top, looking—hoping—that someone would take the seat beside Dawn so he could triumphantly demand a bus of his own. But there were no other seats and no other passengers.

He suddenly wanted very much to go back out to his mother, even though she would say he was being irrational. But then when he caught a glimpse of her through the window, she looked almost as miserable as he felt. He remembered the bear hug with a shiver. It shook his resolve. Timidly he turned to Dawn.

"Is this seat taken?" he asked.

The girl took off her Walkman earphones and stared at the seat a bit, as if looking for someone. She took a long time.

"Doesn't look like it."

Barnsey sat down and made himself comfortable. He got out his own Walkman and arranged his tapes on his lap and thought about the order in which he was going to eat all the junk he had or whether he'd eat a bit of each thing—the chocolate bars, the chips, the Coke—in some kind of order so they all came out even. At home his mother had packed a loganberry soda and some trail mix. He'd keep those for last. Strictly emergency stuff.

Then the bus driver came on board and they were off.

"There's talk of big snow up the valley a way, so I'm gonna light a nice cozy fire," he said. People chuckled. There was already a cozy kind of nighttime we're-stuck-in-this-together mood on the bus. Nobody was drunk or too loud. And the girl beside Barnsey seemed to be completely engrossed in whatever was coming through her earphones.

It was only the way she looked that he had any problem with. The nine earrings, the nose rings, and the Mohawk in particular—orange along the scalp and purple along the crest as if her skull was a planet and the sun was coming up on the horizon of her head. She was about twenty and dressed all in black, with clunky black Doc Martens.[2] But as long as she was just going to listen to her music, then Barnsey would listen to his and everything would be fine.

---

2 **Doc Martens:** an expensive brand of casual shoes

And it was for the first hour or so. By then the bus had truly slipped into a comfortable humming silence. It was about nine, and some people were sleeping. Others were talking softly as if they didn't want to wake a baby in the next room. That's when the mix-up occurred.

There isn't much room in a bus seat. And there wasn't much room on Barnsey's lap. Somehow a couple of his tapes slid off him into the space between him and Dawn, the girl with the horizon on her head, though he didn't know her name yet. The weird thing was, the same thing had happened to her tapes. And the weirdest thing of all was that they both found out at just about the same time.

Barnsey shoved the new Xiphoid Process tape into his machine and punched it on. While he was waiting for the music to start, he dug the cassette out from his backpack and looked again at the hologram cover. The band was standing under lowering skies all around an eerie-looking gravestone. Then if you tipped the cover just right, the guys all seemed to pull back, and there was a hideous ghoul all covered with dirt and worms standing right in the middle of them where the grave marker had been. It was great.

Barnsey pulled a bag of chips from the backpack at his feet, squeezed it so that the pressure in the bag made it pop open, and crunched on a couple of chips as quietly as he could. He was busy enjoying the way the first sour cream and onion chip tastes, and it took him a minute to notice he wasn't hearing anything.

He turned the volume up a bit. Nothing. Then he realized there *was* something. A tinkling noise and a bit of whooshing noise, and a bit of what sounded like rain and some dripping and more tinkling.

Barnsey banged his Walkman. He thought the batteries were dying. Then Dawn changed tapes as well and suddenly yelled, as if she'd just touched a hot frying pan. Some people looked around angrily. The looks on their faces made Barnsey think they had just been waiting for a chance to glare at her. One lady glanced at him, too, in a pitying kind of way, as if to say, Poor young thing. Having to sit beside a banshee[3] like that.

Meanwhile, both of them opened up their Walkmans like Christmas presents. They held their tapes up to the little lights above them to check the titles.

---

3 **banshee:** a female spirit whose appearance foretells death. Here it means an undesirable person.

"Rain Forest with Temple Bells?" Barnsey read out loud.

" 'Scream for Your Supper!' " Dawn read out loud.

Barnsey apologized, nervously. Dawn just laughed. They made the switch, but before Barnsey could even say thank you, the girl suddenly took his tape back.

"Tell you what," she said. "You listen to that fer 'alf a mo, and I'll give this a try. 'kay?"

She had a thick accent, British.

"Okay," said Barnsey, "but I think yours is broken or something."

She took her tape back and tried it. She smiled, and her smile was good. It kind of stretched across her face and curled up at the ends.

"Naa," she said. "Ya just 'av ta listen, mate. Closely, like."

So Barnsey listened closely. He turned it up. There was a rain forest. There were ravens croaking and other birds twittering away. And there were bells. He thought someone was playing them, but after a while he realized that it was just the rain playing them, the wind. He kept waiting for the music to start. He didn't know what the music would be. Any moment a drum would kick in, he thought, then a synthesizer all warbly and a guitar keening high and distorted and a thumping bass and, last of all, a voice. Maybe singing about trees. About saving them.

But no drum kicked in. Maybe the tape *was* broken?

It took him a minute to realize Dawn was tapping him on the shoulder. She had his Xiphoid Process tape in her hand and a cranky look on her face.

"This is killer-diller," she said.

"You like X.P.?" he asked.

"It's rubbish."

Barnsey laughed. Rubbish. What a great word. He pulled out Rain Forest with Temple Bells.

"What ya think?" she asked.

"It's rubbish."

Then they both started to giggle. And now people stared at them as if they were in cahoots and going to ruin the whole trip for everyone. Dawn hit him on the arm to shush him up.

He showed her the hologram cover of the X.P. tape.

"You think it's their mum?" she asked.

"Maybe," he said. He wished he could think of something to say. He just flipped the picture a few times. She leaned toward him. Her hand out.

"Dawn," she whispered.

It took him a minute to realize she was introducing herself. "Barnsey," he whispered back, as if it was a code. He shook her hand.

He offered her some chips. She took the whole bag and made a big deal of holding it up to the light so she could read the ingredients. She shuddered.

"It's a bleedin' chemical plant in 'ere," she said.

"Rubbish," said Barnsey. Then he dug out the trail mix and they both settled down to listen to their own tapes. Barnsey turned X.P. down to 2 because there was no way Dawn would be able to hear her forest with Spice-box wailing on the guitar and Mickey Slick pounding on the drums. After a couple of cuts he switched it off altogether.

He found himself thinking of the time he had traveled with his father out to British Columbia, where he was from, to Denman Island. He remembered the forest there, like nothing he'd ever seen in southern Ontario. Vast and high. It had been a lovely summer day with the light sifting down through the trees. But, he thought, if it rained there, it would sound like Dawn's tape.

He didn't put a tape in his cassette. He left the earphones on and listened to the hum of the bus instead.

▲   ▲   ▲

"It's not so long."

It was the bus driver. Barnsey woke up with his mouth feeling like the inside of a bread box.

There was a stirring all around. People waking, stretching, chattering sleepily and my-my-ing as they looked out the windows. The bus was stopped.

"Will ya lookit that," said Dawn. Her nose was pressed up against the window. Outside was a nothingness of white.

They had pulled off the highway into a football field-sized parking lot. Another bus was parked up ahead. Through the swirling blizzard they could see lots of trucks and cars in the lot. It wasn't the stop Barnsey remembered from previous trips.

Barnsey could see the driver standing outside without his jacket, his shoulders hunched against the driving snow. He was talking to another bus driver, nodding his head a lot and stamping his feet to keep warm. Then he hopped back on the bus and closed the door behind him.

"Seems like we've got ourselves a little unscheduled stop," he said. "The road's bunged up clear through to Mattawa."

Someone asked him a question. Somebody interrupted with another question. The driver did a lot of answering and nodding and shaking his head and reassuring. Barnsey just looked over Dawn's shoulder at the outside, shivering a bit from sleepiness and the sight of all that whirling snow. Dawn smelled nice. Not exotic like the perfume his mother wore, but kind of bracing and clean.

"This here place doesn't have a name," said the driver. People laughed. He was making it all sound like fun. "But the barn there with all the blinking lights is called the Cattle Yard, and the owner says yer'all welcome to come on down and warm yerself up a spell."

Passengers immediately started to get up and stretch and fish around for handbags and sweaters and things. There was an air of excitement on the bus. The Cattle Yard was a big roadhouse painted fire-engine red and lit up with spotlights. It was no ordinary way station.

Still sleepy, Barnsey made no effort to move as people started to file past him pulling on their coats. Dawn still had her nose pressed up against the glass.

"D'ya know where I spent last Christmas?" she said. Barnsey thought for a moment, as if maybe she'd told him and he'd forgotten.

"In Bethlehem," she said.

"The Bethlehem?"

"That's right," she said. "In a bar."

Barnsey looked at Dawn. She was smiling but not like she was fooling. "There are bars in Bethlehem?"

She laughed. "Brilliant bars. Smashing litt'l town is Bethlehem."

Barnsey tried to imagine it.

Then the bus driver was beside him. "Here, you might need this," he said. And with a flick of his fingers he produced the half-a-twenty Barnsey's mother had given him. Barnsey was about to explain that it was meant to be a tip, but the driver waved his hand in protest. "Just don't get yourself all liquored up, son," he said, and then, laughing and clapping Barnsey on the back, he headed out of the bus.

"Wha's that then?" asked Dawn, looking at the half-a-twenty-dollar bill. Barnsey pulled the other half out of his pants pocket and held them side by side.

"Hungry?" he said.

▲ ▲ ▲

And she was hungry. He hadn't realized how skinny she was, but she stored away a grilled cheese sandwich in no time and two pieces of apple pie with ice cream. She ordered hot water and fished a tea bag from deep in her ratty black leather jacket.

"Ginseng, mate," she said. "Nothing illegal."

But Barnsey had only been noticing how stained the tea bag was and the little tab at the end of the string which had strange characters written on it.

It was all so strange. Strange for Barnsey to walk into a place with her, as if they were on a date—a thirteen-year-old and a twenty-year-old. He wondered if people thought she was his sister. He couldn't imagine his parents putting up with the way Dawn looked. She sure turned heads at the Cattle Yard. He wasn't sure if he minded or not. In his burgundy L. L. Bean coat, he didn't exactly look like he belonged in the place, either.

It was a huge smoke-filled bar with moose antlers on the knotty pine walls and two or three big TVs around the room tuned into the Nashville Network. There was a Leafs game on the TV over the bar. Just about everyone was wearing a trucker's hat, and nobody looked like they were leaving until maybe Christmas.

The bus passengers were herded down to one end where a section had been closed off but was now reopened. The bus drivers smoked and made phone calls and made jokes to their passengers about not getting on the wrong bus when they left and ending up in Timbuktu. Through the window and the blizzard of snow, Barnsey watched another bus roll in.

"I saw three ships cum sailin' in," sang Dawn. She was picking at Barnsey's leftover french fries—*chips*, she called them—trying to find ones that didn't have any burger juice on them. She was a vegetarian.

"Bloody heathen," she'd called him when he'd ordered a bacon burger with fries. He loved that.

"I've gotta go find the loo," she said.

"Bloody heathen," he said.

She flicked him on the nose with a chip as she clomped in her Doc Martens. He wondered if it was possible to walk quietly in them.

"Rubbish," he said. He watched her walk through the bar toward the washrooms. Somebody must have said something to her because she suddenly stopped and turned back to a table where five guys in trucking caps were sitting. They looked like all together they probably weighed a ton, but that didn't seem to bother Dawn. She leaned up close to one of them, her fists curled menacingly, and snarled something right at his face.

Barnsey watched in horror, imagining a scene from some movie where the whole place would erupt into a beer-slinging, window-smashing brawl. Instead, the guy whose face she was talking at suddenly roared with laughter and slapped the tabletop. The other four guys laughed, too. One of them ended up spitting half a mug of beer all over his friends. Then Dawn shook hands with her tormentors and sauntered off to the loo, as she called it.

Barnsey felt like he would burst with admiration. He picked up her teacup and smelled the ginseng. It smelled deadly. The writing on the little tab was Indian, he guessed. From India.

He looked around. On the big TV a country songstress with big country hair and dressed in a beautiful country-blue dress was draping silver tinsel on a Christmas tree while she sang about somebody being home for Christmas. Then the image would cut to that somebody in a half-ton truck fighting his way through a blizzard. Same boat we're in, thought Barnsey. Then the image would cut back to the Christmas tree and then to a flashback of the couple walking up a country road with a bouncy dog, having an argument in the rain and so on. Then back to the guy in the truck, the girl by the tree. It was a whole little minimovie.

Barnsey found himself trying to imagine X.P. dressing that same tinselly Christmas tree in that nice living room. But of course the guy in the truck trying to get home for Christmas would be the grim reaper or something, with worms crawling out of its eyes.

Then Dawn came back.

"What did you say to that guy?" Barnsey asked.

She smiled mysteriously. "I told 'im that if 'e'd said what 'e said to me in Afghanistan, 'e'd 'ave to marry me on the spot."

▲ ▲ ▲

It was around eleven before word came through that it was safe to leave. The drivers got everybody sorted out and back on board. Everyone at the Cattle Yard yelled Merry Christmas and held up their beer glasses in a toast. The guy who had been rude to Dawn stood and bowed as she passed by, and she curtsied. Then she made as if she was going to bite off his nose, which made his ton of friends roar again, their fat guts shaking with laughter.

By then Barnsey knew that Dawn had just got back from Nepal, where she'd been traveling with "'er mate" ever since she left Israel, where she'd been working on a kibbutz[4] after arriving there from Bloody Cairo, where she'd had all her kit[5] stolen. Before that she'd been in Ghana and before that art school. Barnsey didn't know what a kit was, or a kibbutz. He wasn't sure where Nepal was, either, or what or who 'er mate might be. But he didn't ask. She'd called him mate, too.

On the bus the excitement of the unscheduled stop soon died down. The roads were only passable so it was slow going. It was kind of nice that the three buses were traveling together. In a convoy, the driver had called it. It sounded reassuring. Soon people were falling asleep, snoring. But not Barnsey. He sat thinking. Trying to imagine working on a flower farm in Israel, the heat, the fragrance of it. Trying to imagine Bethlehem.

"Was it cold?"

"Freezin' at night," she said.

"See any stables?"

She laughed. "No, but I did see a good-sized shed behind a McDonald's."

Barnsey laughed. He tried to imagine the holy family pulling into Bethlehem today and huddling down in a shed out back of a McDonald's. Maybe Joseph would have a Big Mac. But Mary? Probably a vegetarian, he decided.

Quietness again.

"What kind of a store is it your people 'ave, master Barnsey?"

"A gift store," he said.

"Ah, well," said Dawn. "I can imagine a gift store would be busy at Christmas."

Finally, Barnsey dozed off. And the next thing he knew, the bus was slowing down and driving through the deserted streets of North Bay. It was past 2:00 A.M.

"That'll be 'er," said Dawn as they pulled into the bus terminal. Somehow she had recognized his Grandma Barrymore in the little knot of worried folks waiting.

Barnsey just sat drowsily for a minute while people stirred around him. He felt like he weighed a ton.

---

4 **kibbutz:** a work commune

5 **kit:** traveling gear

"Get on with ya," said Dawn in a cheery voice. And she made a big joke of shoving him and roughhousing him out of his seat as if he was Dumbo the elephant. Then she gathered up all his wrappers and cans and threw them at him, saying, "'Ere—lookit this! Yer not leavin' this for me, I'ope." Barnsey found himself, weak with laughter, herded down the aisle. At the door he said good-bye and hoped that her trip to Vancouver would be nothing but rubbish the whole way. Grandma Barrymore was standing at the foot of the bus stairs. Much to her surprise, Dawn grabbed Barnsey by the head and scrubbed it hard with her knuckle.

"In Afghanistan, you'd have to marry me for that," said Barnsey.

"Toodle-oo, mate," said Dawn, blowing him a kiss. She blew one at Grandma Barrymore, too.

▲ ▲ ▲

Dawn would arrive in Vancouver on Christmas Eve. Barnsey thought of her often over the next couple of days. He'd check his watch and imagine her arriving in Winnipeg, although all he knew of Winnipeg was the Blue Bombers football stadium which he'd seen on TV. And then Regina and Calgary. He imagined the three buses like wise men still traveling across the country in a convoy. But as much as Barnsey thought about Dawn, he gave up trying to talk to anyone about her. Grandma had seen her but only long enough to get the wrong impression. And when Barnsey tried to tell his cousins about her, it came out like a cartoon, with her wacky hair and her fat black boots. He couldn't get Dawn across to them—the *life* of her—only the image of her, so he stopped trying.

There was a lot to do, anyway. His cousins had arranged a skating party and Grandma wanted him to go shopping with her and help with some chores around the house. He enjoyed all the attention she showered on him. She spoiled him rotten just the way she'd spoiled his father rotten, she liked to say. But he'd never noticed it quite so much as this year. Anything he looked at, she asked him if he wanted it. It was spooky.

Then it was Christmas morning. It was a four-hour drive from Ottawa. His parents would arrive by 1:00 P.M. and that's when the celebration would start. When he saw his father's Mustang coming up the driveway at 10:30 A.M., Barnsey knew something was wrong.

He didn't go to the door. He watched from the window. They should have come in the big car. But there wasn't any they. Just his dad.

"Matthew, go help your dad with his parcels," said Grandma.

"No," said Barnsey. He was remembering the last time he had looked at his mother in the bus terminal, through the window. The look on her face. "It won't be so long," she had said.

It wasn't that his mother was sick or there was some problem at the store; they would have phoned. Barnsey's mind grew icy sharp. Everything was suddenly clear to him. He could see a trail of incidents leading to this if he thought about it. You just had to tilt life a bit, and there was a whole other picture.

His parents weren't very talkative. They didn't chatter; they didn't argue. And yet in the moments while his father unpacked the trunk of his salt-stained Mustang and made his way back and forth up the path Barnsey had shoveled so clean just the night before, Barnsey could hear in his head all the signs and hints stretching back through the months—how far, he wasn't sure. Right up to now, the past few days, with Grandma so attentive. Spoiling him rotten.

Then his father was in the living room, still in his coat, waiting for Barnsey to say something. His face didn't look good but to Barnsey he didn't look anywhere near bad enough, all things considered. Grandma Barrymore was standing behind him with her hand on her son's shoulder. She looked very sad. They waited. Barnsey looked out the window. Old-fashioned lace curtains hung across the living-room window. They were always there, even when the drapes were open. Barnsey stood between the lace and the cold glass. He turned and looked at his grandma through the veil of the curtain.

"I wish you'd told me," he said.

"She didn't know, Matthew," said his father. "Not for sure."

The ball was back in his court. That was the way his parents were with him. Lots of room. His father would not press him. He could wait forever and his father would never start saying stuff like "I'm sorry, honey," or "It's all for the better," or "Your mother still loves you, Matthew." Barnsey could wait forever and he wouldn't see his father cry. He would have done his crying already, if he had any crying to do. His parents didn't hold much with spontaneity.

He glanced at his father in his black coat and white silk scarf. He wanted him to do something.

Barnsey stared out the window.

"When did you get the ski rack," he said.

"When I needed something to carry skis."

There was a pair of skis on the top of the car. Rossignols.[6]

"They're yours," said his father. "I couldn't exactly wrap them."

Barnsey had been wanting downhill skis. And one of the large boxes piled in the hall was probably a good pair of ski boots. His parents would have read consumer reports about this. Even while they were breaking up.

"Your mother is hoping maybe you'll go on a skiing trip with her later in the holidays. Maybe Vermont."

"That would be nice," said Barnsey. Then he left the window and went to his room. His father didn't follow. It was his way of showing respect. He didn't say that; he didn't have to. He was there for him. He didn't say that, either, but it was something Barnsey had heard often. "We're here for you, chum."

Barnsey stayed in his room a long time, long enough to hear both sides of the new X.P. tape he hadn't had time to listen to on the bus. He flipped the cassette cover again and again. The ghoul glowed and vanished. Glowed and vanished.

Then his mother phoned. They had probably worked all this out, too.

"Must have been a terrible shock . . .

"Decided it was best this way . . .

"We couldn't dissolve the partnership in time for the shopping season . . .

"Couldn't see us play-acting our way through Christmas . . ."

Barnsey listened. Said the right things.

"Do you think we could head down to Mount Washington for a long weekend?" said his mother. "Give those new skis a workout?"

"They aren't new," said Barnsey.

"They sure are," said his mother. "They're the best."

"There's a lot of snow between here and Ottawa," said Barnsey. It took his mother a minute to realize it was a joke. A lame kind of joke.

Then, with plans tentatively set and the call over and his mother's voice gone, Barnsey joined his father and his father's mother in the living room. They both gave him hugs.

"You okay?" his father asked.

"Yes."

"You want to talk now? Or later?"

6 **Rossignols:** a high-quality brand of skis

"Later," he said.

"I think we all need a sherry,"[7] said Grandma. She poured Barnsey a glass. He like the idea better than the sherry.

They ate lunch and then, since it was Christmas, they sat in the living room opening presents. Barnsey kept glancing at his father, expecting to see a little telltale tear or something. But all he ever glimpsed were the concerned looks his father was giving him.

He took his father's place as the hander-outer. When he came to his own present for his mother, he said, "Where should I put this?" His father piled the package on a chair in the hall.

Barnsey wasn't looking forward to Christmas dinner at his aunt's. His father had already taken that into consideration and would stay with him at Grandma's, if he liked. They'd make something special, just the two of them. But when he phoned to explain things, his sister wouldn't hear of them not coming, and his cousins got on the phone and begged Barnsey to come and try out their new computer game and in the end he went. Nobody talked about his mother not being there, at least not while Barnsey was around. Everyone was really considerate.

In bed he lay thinking about what kind of a place his mother would live in. She was the one leaving the relationship, so she was the one leaving the house. Barnsey wondered whether there would be a room for him or whether she'd just make up a couch when he came to visit. Then he wondered if his father would stay in Ottawa or move back to the west coast. He lay trying to think of as many things as could possibly go wrong so that he wouldn't be surprised by anything.

"I just wish someone had told me," he said.

"We'll turn it around, Matthew," his father had said when he came to say good-night. "We'll make this into a beginning."

Was that from some kind of a book? How could he say that? Couldn't he tell the difference between a beginning and an ending?

There wasn't another man in his mother's life. His father hadn't found another woman.

"At least it isn't messy," his father said. He needn't have bothered. Nothing they ever did was messy.

In his sleep, Barnsey escaped. He found himself back on the bus.

"Rubbish," Dawn kept saying, and she pounded her fist into her palm every time she said it. Then the man in the seat ahead of them turned

---

7 **sherry:** a type of wine

around, and it was the guy who had been in the country video heading home in his half-ton through a blizzard to his tinsel-happy lady.

"Rubbish," he said. And then all of Xiphoid Process, who were *also* on the bus, turned around in their seats, pounding their fists and saying, "Rubbish. Rubbish. Rubbish." Soon the bus driver joined in and the whole bus sang a "Hallelujah Chorus" of "Rubbish, rubbish, rubbish."

Barnsey woke up, his head spinning. All he could think about was rubbish. He thought about the talk he had to have with his father that day. His father wouldn't insist, but he would be expecting it. He would say all the right things and, before Barnsey knew it, *he* would be saying all the right things, too. They'd talk it out. Get things out in the open. It would all make perfect sense.

Rubbish.

So he left.

He didn't pack a bag, only stuffed a couple of extra things in his backpack. He wasn't sure what a ticket to Vancouver cost, but it didn't matter. He had his bank card. He had no idea what he was going to do and he didn't care. He would not run away like his mother, carefully planning it all out first. How far did that get you?

And so, by nine o'clock on Boxing Day[8] morning, he was at the bus terminal, a ticket in his pocket, sitting, waiting. He had his Walkman with him and he rooted around in his backpack for a tape other than X.P. He didn't think he could take that right now.

He had five or six tapes in the bottom of his bag. He hadn't emptied it since the trip. He pulled them out one by one: Alice in Chains, Guns 'n' Roses, Nirvana, Rain Forest with Temple Bells—

Rain Forest with Temple Bells?

Barnsey stared at the tape. He must have packed it up in the dark of the bus without noticing. Then he saw a piece of paper sticking out of the edge of the cassette. He opened the cassette and took out a folded-up note written in pencil.

dear barnsey this is for the meal and for the fun and for when the rubbish gets to be too much but you're snoring while i write this so maybe i'll shove the note in your gob!!! no i won't i'll hide it and it'll be your xmas present from dawn xox

Barnsey found himself shaking. He read the note again and again. He smelled it—trying to catch her scent—and held it and then folded it up

---

8 **Boxing Day:** the day after Christmas, a Canadian and British holiday

carefully and put it back in the cassette. He took out the tape and put it on. He closed his eyes and let the rain on the bells and the ravens and the smaller birds and the ferns and the trees and the wind fill his ears.

How crazy it had been to wait for the music to start. You had to supply your own. Make it out of what was there. Because there was more than the rain forest. Beyond his earphones there were people talking, departure announcements, a man waxing the floor—they were all part of the music.

Then suddenly there was a voice much closer.

"Matthew," said the voice, and Matthew became part of the music. "Matthew." Barnsey opened his eyes and his father was sitting there beside him. He touched his son's knee so tentatively, it was as if he was afraid the boy might break, like some fragile ornament from the gift store. Barnsey wondered if he would break, but he wouldn't. He was going to Vancouver to find Dawn. He stared at his father, who could not know this.

His father was in his black coat and white scarf, but his hair was a complete mess. Barnsey had never seen his father out of the house unshaven and looking such a mess. His eyes were the worst mess of all.

"You look scared," said Barnsey. His father nodded. He didn't speak. He was waiting, giving Barnsey space. Then Barnsey looked closer into those wrecked eyes and suddenly it occurred to him that his father wasn't giving him space. He just didn't have any idea what to say or do. He was a million miles from the safe world of the gift store. He looked as if all his careful plans had fallen through.

Barnsey wanted to shake him, to knuckle his head, to throw stuff at him, laughing and shoving. To wake him up.

"Here," he said. He took off his earphones and put them on his father.

"What is it?" his father asked. "Is it broken?"

"No," said Barnsey. "Listen closely."

He watched his father listening. Barnsey listened, too. He didn't need the earphones to hear it. ❧

Untitled

Langston Hughes

I loved my friend.
He went away from me.
There's nothing more to say.
The poem ends,
Soft as it began —
I loved my friend.

RESPONDING TO CLUSTER ONE

WHAT IS A FRIEND?

Thinking Skill DEFINING

1. In the poem "For Friendship" on page 4, the sharply contrasting words "chain" and "garland" are used to describe the relationships between friends. Describe some qualities of friendship these two words **symbolize**, or represent. Then use two contrasting words of your own to describe friendship.

2. Unity between friends is the **theme** of the poem "For Heidi with Blue Hair." Besides dying her own hair, what could Heidi's friend have done to show her support?

3. Several of the pieces in this cluster are about friendships between humans and animals. In your opinion, who makes a better friend, an animal or a person? Explain your response.

4. Write three words to **define**, or describe, the friendship in each of the selections in this cluster. Try not to repeat the defining words you use. You might use a chart such as the one below.

Selection	Three Words That Define the Friendship
Dirk	
For Heidi With Blue Hair	
Joe King	
Dawn	
Untitled Poem	

5. The power of Langston Hughes' untitled poem lies less in what it says than in what it doesn't say. We only know that the speaker loved a friend who left him. Can two people remain friends at a distance? Be prepared to explain your answer.

Writing Activity: Defining Friendship

Create your own definition of friendship. The chart you created in question 4 above may help you. Write your definition in either prose or poetry.

A Strong Definition

- begins by stating the term to be defined
- lists the various characteristics or qualities of the term
- provides examples
- ends with a final definition

CLUSTER TWO

What Would You Do for a Friend?
Thinking Skill   ANALYZING

KIMCHEE AND CORN BREAD

HELIE LEE AND STEPHANIE COVINGTON

Life with Stephanie

Stephanie's like a White person, I thought when I asked her to be my roommate. She had been a regular in the coffee shop that I managed, and we had struck up an easy friendship. So when I found out she was looking for an apartment at about the same time I had begun dreaming of larger quarters, I suggested we live together.

Stephanie was all-American like me. She with her groovy A-line-cut hair and Chilean man. Me with my retro bob with the curling-iron flip and South Carolina boyfriend. But immediately after we moved in, I realized Stephanie's rich chocolate color was not merely flesh-shallow. As I rolled out my thin mattress on the ground and set up my Buddhist altar, Stephanie transformed her whitewashed room into something "out of Africa," with bright-golden sponged walls and dried flowers tossed randomly. Along the earth-toned floor, books by Maya Angelou, Toni Morrison and Sonia Sanchez—authors I'd never heard of before—were piled high like trees. When I asked Stephanie who Maya was, she glared at me as if I had just noticed that she's Black. She promptly chopped down a stack and tossed them on my bed for me to read.

In the dining area, she nailed up a picture of herself and her young single mother styling matching Afros, and another one of her mom marching in front of the White House in her far-out bell-bottoms during the 1970's. How cool was that! In the 1970's, my own parents had been too busy immigrating to America, the land of the free and beds with legs, and too involved with overseeing our homework assignments to think of marching.

From a box marked "kitchen," Stephanie pulled out a six-months' supply of Jiffy corn-bread mix as I plugged in my two rice cookers. "Two rice cookers?" Stephanie commented. "You really are Oriental."

"No, I'm Asian," I corrected her. "Rugs are Oriental."

"Where should I hang my mud cloth?" Stephanie inquired.

"Hey, every colored person has a vest or a hat made from that," I said proudly, recognizing the ethnic fabric.

"Colored?" Stephanie repeated incredulously. "The word *colored* went out with the desegregation of toilets."

The day of the O.J. verdict, our racial distinctions glowed to blinding pigments of black and yellow. Stephanie, with her newly pierced nose, radically shaved head and sista girlfriends, crowded round the TV. She cheered and gyrated her privileged Black woman's butt as the verdict was read. I stayed seated on my less-developed Asian one.

"You really believe he didn't do it?" I asked, mortified.

"I didn't say he was innocent, but it's about time a brother didn't get beaten by the man," she declared.

"Who's 'the man'?" I finally asked. I had heard the phrase repeatedly at a Black poetry forum that I attended with Stephanie. Stephanie and her sista friends all burst into hysterical laughter.

"The man," Stephanie managed between giggles, "the man is the White racist system that designed the three-strikes-you're-out law to keep us down like slaves." More seriously, she added, "Your people have it much easier here."

"Not true," I said hotly. "Koreans picked sugarcane in Hawaii. We were indentured servants.[1] Your people aren't the only ones who suffered. The difference is we don't sulk and blame everyone else. My people pool money together and start businesses to support our families."

"Exactly," Stephanie shot back. "It's your people who come into our neighborhoods with bad attitudes and get rich off our people."

---

1 **indentured servants:** poor people forced by contract to work for others

Quickly, it became her people, my people and "the man." Division, segregation, anger. There was so much each of us didn't understand about the other's history or experience in America. If we were to survive as roommates, it would be necessary to educate ourselves.

So I took Stephanie over for a Korean Thanksgiving, which included extended relatives spanning four generations. It was an unprecedented event for everyone. Stephanie was the first *heuk-in-sah-lam* (Black person) my family had ever come into direct contact with without the separation of a counter or bulletproof partition between them. Like a dutiful roommate, I had prepped her beforehand: Take off your shoes at the door (meaning: Wear matching socks with no holes). It's not customary to hug, so don't be offended. And they'll ask all sorts of personal questions. Koreans aren't into privacy, so just don't bring up marriage, for my sake.

My family smiled politely and stared at Stephanie's every move. "Good," my mother praised as Stephanie pressed her palms together and prayed over her full plate of kimchee[2] and rice. In that one evening, my friend prayed and ate her way into my family's hearts; she turned my family's preconceived fears and prejudices of *heuk-in-sah-lam* 180 affectionate degrees.

For me, when I'm with Stephanie's family or peers, I'm very conscious of my actions, because for many of them I am the first Korean they've befriended. It's an enormous burden sometimes, but Stephanie and I are in a unique living situation, and we have a responsibility not only to ourselves, but also to our communities. We still debate O.J. and the Korean-grocer issues, but whenever the anger escalates, we call each other Soon-yi and Shaniqua,[3] and the anger dissolves into laughter. Sure, some people might consider our little joke racist, but who would dare accuse us of being politically incorrect? We laugh all the time over a banquet of Korean and soul food. Today Stephanie makes killer kimchee, and I have mastered the recipe for corn bread. And no longer does my roommate question the need for two rice cookers. Stephanie eats more rice than I do!

2 **kimchee:** a Korean dish of spicy fermented cabbage

3 **Soon-yi and Shaniqua:** common names for Korean and African American girls, respectively

Life with Helie

Helie annihilated the stereotypes of the docile, subservient[4] Asian woman I'd grown up viewing on television. Sporting funky retro clothing, a *Friends* haircut, hip huggers exposing her aerobicized stomach and a "take no prisoners" attitude, she was nobody's geisha girl.[5] Moving (surprisingly well) to the beat, Helie was fierce. Her occasional choppy speech hinted that she was Korean-born, but to me she was as "White bread" as my more radical friends accused me of being, despite my natural hair, nose ring and girl-from-the-'hood upbringing. Helie was the banana to my Oreo—or so I thought.

Harboring a sneaking suspicion that Helie, like all Koreans, quietly planned to own America, I took her up on her offer to live together. On moving day I arrived at our new apartment with my belongings to find a refrigerator already full of kimchee, a spicy fermented cabbage that to my untrained nose smelled like reason enough to fumigate the house. In the bedroom she had placed her mattress on a bamboo floor mat, hung scrolls of bamboo art on the walls and set out candles everywhere. The effect was sparsely Eastern.

Once we were settled in, we looked around the apartment with satisfaction. My African-American art, African textiles and boxes of Jiffy corn-bread mix coexisted with Helie's Buddhist altar, rice cookers, green tea and chopsticks. We soon used chopsticks to eat everything, including my corn bread.

"We're a family now," Helie cheered, then proceeded to educate me on my newly acquired responsibilities—such as informing her of when I planned to return home late.

"I don't answer to anybody, not even my mother," I protested.

"Stephanie," she groaned, "sometimes you can be too Western." Patiently, she explained: "In my culture, everything is a function of strengthening the family unit, not the individual. I'm always conscious of how my actions will affect my family. You should be, too."

I hated it when Helie selectively chose to exercise her Eastern-born status, but I didn't press the issue. I figured I'd just continue to live as I always had, coming and going as I pleased. But a few weeks later when Helie

4 **docile:** easily managed; **subservient:** submissive
5 **geisha girl:** a girl who is trained to be an entertaining companion

didn't come home, I spent the entire night sick with worry about whether she was all right. Helie had simply neglected to inform me that she would sleep the night at her parents' house. It was a subtle but potent lesson.

Later, when Helie had a novel published and began her book tour, I casually suggested that she choose a signing for me to attend.

"*What?*" she gagged. "All of them!"

"Excuse me?" I said, attitude exploding from my swiveling shoulders and neck.

"You are my family," Helie said, growing emotional, "and just as I expect them to be at each of my readings so should you. Besides, it's your duty as my roommate."

"Helie," I said, sounding more indignant than I'd planned, "when I write a play, I ask people to attend one performance. One." The daughter of a single working parent, I knew my mother's presence at my events was something of a luxury. After all, she had bills to pay. But Helie wasn't having it.

"Wouldn't it be great, Stephanie, if you expected me to attend every performance and I did?"

True to her word, Helie supported me in all my endeavors. Shortly after I met her, she converted from her family's adopted Christianity to her native Buddhism; she is still terrified to tell her family that she chants instead of prays. Nevertheless, she often comes with me to my church, a tear-the-roof-off-catch-the-spirit-meditate-and-celebrate house of worship. At first she was overwhelmed by the fervor, missing the humble murmurs of the congregants from the church of her childhood. But the music, the preaching and the fellowship soon won her over. "This is more like a concert," she said one Sunday as she danced jubilantly in the aisle.

When I introduced Helie to Jonathan, a fine brother from the 'hood, I expected them to get along effortlessly. They are both talented writers, and I thought the world of each of them. But I was being naive. Jonathan had had too many racially charged encounters with Korean grocers to greet Helie without suspicion. Once while he was in New York attending a screening, he and some friends stopped at a local Korean grocery to buy some fruit. He was dressed in sweats and sneakers, and the grocer immediately picked up a broom and came from behind the counter to shoo Jonathan and his friends out of the store. He questioned Helie's connection to "those people."

Helie's first response was to defend the grocers. The ensuing game of verbal tennis lasted hours, with Helie and Jonathan vying with each other to prove their group's suffering superior. But in the process, Helie managed to humanize the grocers for Jonathan, pointing out that they were acting based on racial stereotypes widely perpetuated in the media. And Jonathan managed to bring home to Helie the extent to which he had been dehumanized by the racial misconceptions of the grocers.

Helie's commitment to cross-cultural understanding was evident when she invited me to a kimchee Thanksgiving with her family and carefully instructed me on acceptable dress, behavior and forbidden topics of conversation—mainly her boyfriends. I knew that in the eyes of Helie's family, career accomplishment paled next to an unmarried status.

"You rotten fruit! Your time running short!" her father had once bellowed into the phone.

Helie raced into my room, flinging herself across my bed. "I can't believe my worth is measured by my marital status," she screeched. "Isn't this America?"

Although my feminist mother had cautioned me about the dangers of depending on men for my self-worth, I didn't completely dismiss Helie's parents, because my own biological clock[6] was starting to tick.

"You are American," I told her. "Your parents live in America, but they're Korean and they cling to their traditions for fear of extinction."

"How come you don't think they're insane?" she questioned.

"They're not my parents," I chuckled.

My own mother and I are more like friends and confidantes than mother and daughter, so when Helie heard us discussing everything from birth control to communism, she was more than a little surprised. But over time, being privy to my close bond with my mother has altered Helie's relationship with her parents. She has become more intimate and open about her life, and recently even took them to dinner with her new boyfriend—the first Korean man she has dated.

Helie and I still argue about the oppression our respective races have endured. I remind her that she has the luxury of memory: Her family can remember being royalty, while mine is continually reminded of slave auctions and laws determining us three-quarters human. But born of cultures an ocean apart, the beliefs and experiences that separate us are slowly becoming less like a sea of differences and more like a bridge to understanding and sisterhood. ∾

---

6 **biological clock:** an internal timing mechanism that prompts some women to wish to become mothers

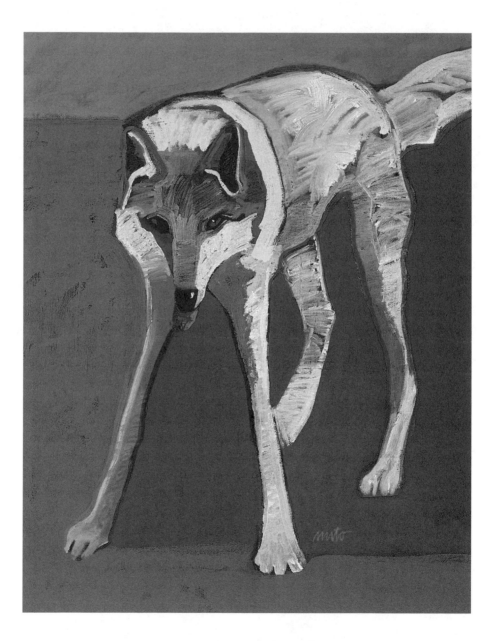

JONES AND THE STRAY

MARTHA SOUKUP

Jones blew hard to see how far out her breath would fog. Pretty far. It seemed to her it must be possible—if the wind were still and there were the same amount of moisture in the air—to guess the temperature by the length of the breath cloud you could blow. If you filled your lungs with the same amount of air and blew just as hard.

Well, that was an awful lot of ifs. Maybe not.

When you were in Alaska in the winter, you always knew it was cold, anyway, and you'd better never let yourself forget it if you wanted to stay alive.

She was rattling at the doorknob of her warehouse. Jones called it her warehouse; whoever's warehouse it actually was wasn't using it for anything. It was a small, wind-leaky, smelly building, thrown together years ago out of corrugated steel.

What was important was that no one had ever turned off the electricity, and that the lock would give if you jiggled it just right. Of course she didn't have the key.

"Come on, door," Jones said, making two more puffs of frosty breath that drifted back past her ear.

The doorknob felt cold even through the glove of her heatsuit. The suit's charge was wearing down. She'd taken off the big knit glove she usually wore over the thin heatsuit glove, and was holding it in the other knit glove. She wore lots of layers of wool and polyester over the suit, to hold in heat and save the charge. And to make her look bigger, and more anonymous.

She had brought the heatsuit with her from Seattle, along with all the money she had been able to scrounge in a hurry. That was all she had when she left. Her name she acquired a day or two later. She made it up on the long bus trip north, right after she cut her hair short and shaggy in a diner restroom. "Jones." If you said it fast and gruff, maybe no one'd notice exactly who was under all those clothes, especially if you were tall for your age.

Not if you didn't give them too much time to look at you.

"Come on!" she whispered urgently, and the lock slipped, the door opened.

She gave one quick glance behind her and ducked inside.

It was even darker here than it was outside. A little bit of moonlight came in through the cracks in the wall panels. Jones found the light switch. She crossed her fingers, hoping the lights would come on. They did. There was still electricity.

It was funny how you never noticed how tight your shoulders were until they relaxed. Jones turned the lights off again quickly, so that no one would see them, and hurried to the far corner of the warehouse. She felt with her hand for the electrical outlet. With her other hand she took the heavy square transformer from one of her many pockets. She plugged the little lead from the transformer into the suit's connector under her armpit. She plugged the big lead into the electrical outlet in the concrete floor.

She lay back awkwardly against the crinkled wall. The heatsuit wasn't really designed to be recharged while you were still wearing it. You were supposed to be indoors someplace warm, letting it charge back up overnight on a table somewhere while you were in a nice soft bed under all the covers.

Jones reached inside her layers of clothes to a big pocket and found dinner, a plastic bag from inside a cereal box, half-full of puffed corn. She leaned on her left elbow and started eating it with her right hand. The crunch of the cereal was loud and satisfying. She settled in and let her gaze drift across the blackness.

A pair of eyes was looking at her from the near corner of the warehouse.

Jones gasped before she could stop it and clutched her cereal bag close. She drew herself up against the wall as far as she could without unplugging herself, and felt inside her pockets for the long steel wrench she carried there.

"Who's there?" she said loudly in her deepest, gruffest growl.

Silence for a moment.

"Bad," came a thin little voice. "Bad run bad boy hungry food stay away food."

"What?" said Jones, forgetting for a moment in her surprise to use her Jones voice. She found the wrench.

"Bad," the voice said again. "Bad boy dangerous stay away bite bad food hungry food please."

It didn't sound like a man's voice or a woman's voice or a kid's voice. It sounded like a computer, like the computer in class when she still went to school, or the computer her friend Cary used to play games on. Under the voice she could hear the wet sound of heavy breathing.

The eyes were big and round, with a greenish blue glow in the tiny glint of moonlight. They blinked and stared at her.

Jones thought he must have been in there much longer than she'd been, and his eyes would be better adjusted; but no one could see very well in here. She yanked the plug from her suit, dropped her food, and stood with the wrench held high, trying to look big in all her clothes.

"Leave now and there won't be trouble!" she cried in her best mean man's voice.

He barked. Jones almost dropped the wrench.

"Go away go away bad bite bad boy bad dog mean bite go," said the thin computer voice.

"Dog?" said Jones. She squinted, and could barely make out its shaggy gray shape. Lowering the wrench, but holding it tightly, she took a step forward.

The dog whined, and at the same time the voice said, "Bad go scared go bad bad bad bite food please scared." It scrunched back as far as it could go in the corner, whimpering.

"Poor dog," Jones said. "Poor thing, I won't hurt you."

Now she could make out its voder collar. She'd seen rich people walking poodles that were wearing those. The collars had little computers in them that could translate a dog's brain waves into words. It took a lot of training for dogs to use them, and they were expensive. This dog seemed, in the gloom, as scruffy and scared as any stray she'd ever seen, but it must have a rich owner, to afford both the collar and the genetic work that improved its verbal skills so it could use it. She took another slow step forward.

The dog whimpered again. It said, through the collar, "Back bad mean dog bite bite back." Then it moaned and said, "Scared hungry scared."

"It's okay," she said gently. She walked backward, feeling for the cereal bag with her foot. She put the wrench on the floor and took a handful of cereal, holding it out in front of her. "See? Here's some food. It's okay."

The dog was silent, but it stared at her hand.

Jones crouched down, tiptoeing on her haunches to the dog, with the food held out. Now she was right in front of it.

The dog was so still it could have been a stuffed animal. Its eyes looked up from the food to her face. "It's okay," she said, almost whispering. "It's okay. I'm a friend. It's okay."

The dog didn't take its eyes off hers, but then its muzzle was in her hand, its breath warm and moist through the mesh of her heatsuit glove. It licked and ate up the cereal with delicate little movements of its mouth, staring at her.

"See? It's okay. I'm a friend." She reached out to touch its head and the dog ducked away. Jones felt hurt. Then she thought it must still be scared. "It's okay," she said again. She dug through her pockets and found some pretzels, and put them on the floor in front of the dog. "You can have whatever you want."

The dog ate the pretzels. She watched. She could see it better, now that she was close and her eyes had adjusted. It was one of those pretty white dogs. She knew their name: a Samoyed.[1] When they were puppies they looked like toys, with their black button eyes and their fluffy fur and tails. This one was not a little puppy, but it was not full grown, and its fur was dingy and matted with dirt.

"I'm Jones," she said to the dog. "Jones." She patted her chest.

The dog finished eating. It looked at her again. "Ohnz," it said.

"Jones."

"Gohnz. Ohnz. Bones."

Jones laughed. "Not bones. Jones."

"Shones. Jones."

"Jones. Good, yes, Jones."

Carefully, Jones reached out and stroked its head. The dog let her do it. Encouraged, she rubbed its ear and neck. She couldn't remember the last time she'd petted a dog. But there weren't a lot of nice things she remembered—and plenty of things she didn't intend to remember—from before she'd left Seattle.

1 **Samoyed:** a breed of cream or white colored sled dogs

The dog yelped. She pulled back her hand. "What's wrong?" There was something sticky on her glove. She looked at it. "You're bleeding!"

"Hurt run away bad boy hurt," the dog said. She reached to see where the blood was. The dog cringed away.

"It's okay," Jones said. "I'm your friend. I want to see where you're hurt."

She put her hand on its neck and pulled the dog gently around to look at its other side. It whimpered softly, and its collar said, "Hurt bad no please," but it let her do it.

A piece of the dog's skin hung, torn and wet looking, from its flank. Jones' throat felt funny when she saw it; she had to swallow, hard. She made herself look. It was roughly the shape of a triangle, torn from the top, hanging down at the bottom. The flank where the skin had ripped was raw and unpleasant to see.

"What happened?" she asked the dog. "How did you do this? How did you hurt yourself?"

"Hurt," the dog said. It had stopped whimpering, and it looked at her as though it expected something. "Hurt."

"How did you hurt yourself?" she asked again.

"Run away bad dog," it said. "Run away bad master. Hide. Hide inside catch hurt catch pull hurt."

"Catch what? Hurt where?"

The dog looked along the wall of the warehouse toward the door. She looked where it was looking, and could see, just a few feet away, that a join where two sheets of steel had been welded together had come loose. The tear in the wall was only a few inches wide. The dog must have forced its way in through it.

"Did you hurt yourself coming through that hole?" She pointed. "That hole? That hole hurt you?"

"Yes hurt hide inside hide run away yes."

"You poor thing," Jones said again. She hugged it around the neck, hearing its breath in her ear. "Poor dog, why are you hiding?"

"Hide."

"Why?"

"Bad dog run away hide."

"I don't think you're a bad dog," Jones said. When the dog heard "bad dog" it cringed. "No no," she said. "Good dog. You're a good dog. Why did you run away?"

"Hit bad dog hit shout hit run away run away," the dog said.

"Did your master hit you?" Jones asked, feeling her cheeks burn with outrage. Just thinking of it made her want to hit someone back, though she'd promised herself she would never do that.

"Hit bad dog," it said.

"Bad master," Jones said. Her eyes stung.

"Bad master," said the dog.

She made herself calm down. She didn't want to upset the dog. She petted it quietly for a while. "We have to get you fixed," she said. She winced. "Not fixed fixed, I mean we have to get your wound fixed."

"Fix," said the dog. "Help."

"I don't know how to get you help," Jones said. She remembered a veterinary clinic a little to the side of town. How could she just go in there with a runaway dog—her, a runaway herself? They wouldn't be open until morning anyway.

"Jones fix," said the dog.

"Oh, no," Jones said. "I can't fix it." Runaway kids were sent home. Her face was probably on milk cartons. They could look inside their databanks and figure out where to send her back. Freezing in a shed would be better than that.

"Jones fix."

"Sweetie, I don't know how to, I don't have medicine and tools, I can't do it, honey—what is your name?"

The dog was quiet.

"Your name?" Jones said, very clearly.

"Name no. Master shout name bad bad name no. Name bad."

That was almost funny. "You and me, we've got a lot in common. Should I give you a name? Do you want to pick a name?"

The dog looked confused. "Jones fix."

"Okay," Jones said. "Um. Okay. Um. How about Diogenes? He went away from home to find an honest man. I read it in a book about old Greek philosophers. They didn't say if he ever found one." The dog put its head in her lap. "Diogenes?" She said it slowly and carefully: *Dye Ah John Eez.*

The dog tried the name. "Ah geez."

"Ah-geez," Jones agreed. It wasn't the dumbest name she'd ever heard, and the dog was the only one in the world who had it.

"Cold," said Ah-geez. "Hurt cold." The computer voice was calm and ordinary, every word coming out the same. But the dog was beginning to tremble.

"Oh, lord," said Jones. "I can't do anything until morning. What if you've gotten infected? I think if you're sick you have to be specially careful to stay warm." The dog's pelt looked warm, but the place it was torn looked fragile and dangerous. With her heatsuit still working, covering her up from her toes to most of her face, she hadn't thought how painful the freezing air would be on the wound. "Okay," she said. "Okay."

She took off all her many layers of clothes, from the biggest on the outside to the smallest on the inside. She unzipped her heatsuit. The cold air hit her like a fist. "Oh my pete's sake geez!" she said. She hurried back into all her other clothes. It was cold without the heatsuit. She wondered if she could get through a night that cold.

"Here you go," she said. "You have to help me get this over you."

Ah-geez looked uncomprehending, but when she lifted the dog up to try to get its back legs into the legs of the suit, it shifted itself around to help. She pulled the suit up slowly. When she got to the torn part, she winced and put the skin back carefully in place, figuring it had to be less dirty than the inside of her suit. Ah-geez yelped when she touched the wound, then was still, breathing hard.

Jones got the front legs into the heatsuit's arms. She left the suit's hood and mask down, since they wouldn't fit over a dog's face. It all made a lumpy weird shape, a lumpy shape she was perhaps the first person ever to discover. Dog inside heatsuit.

"Better?" she said.

"No cold," Ah-geez said.

"Good," she said.

"Good Jones Jones good," the dog said.

"You're welcome," she said. "Now we wait until morning, and then I'll think of something."

Shivering, she huddled up against the dog's unwounded side and waited for the next dark morning. The dog slept, kicking softly, as dogs do, when it dreamed.

Jones fought to stay awake. She kept watch all night, just like hundreds of nights in Seattle, worrying her way into the next day.

▲   ▲   ▲

The sun didn't come up properly in Alaska in the winter. It clung to the horizon, like sunrise all day. So the streetlights were on and it still felt like night when Jones struggled toward the vet clinic, arms full of lumpy dog.

She wished the streetlights would just short out, make everything as dark as could be. She felt obvious and exposed, everything she had run north not to be.

Mostly she felt exhausted. She could carry Ah-geez, but the dog felt heavier with every step she took. She couldn't shift her arms around without worrying about hurting the torn part of its flank.

She had turned the suit off before leaving the shed, but the dog still felt hot, very hot, too hot. That was what had made up her mind. Ah-geez was sick. There had to be an infection for the dog to be that hot, so much hotter than when she had first found it.

A woman was unlocking the door of the clinic when Jones staggered up. She turned and saw Jones and her bundle. "Good morning," she said, as though a skinny shortish person in a lot of clothes, carrying a mis-shapen bulk of heatsuit with a dog's head panting out of it, was a sight she saw every day.

"Hi," said Jones, and was terrified. She forced her nerves down. "Are you the animal doctor?"

"I am," said the woman. "Doctor Kozlowski. Is that your dog?"

"No," said Jones. "Yes. I mean—" She'd had something all planned to say, something to maybe throw them off and keep them from looking for her before she could be on a bus and going somewhere else. But it all fell out of her mind. Months of not talking to anyone, silently spending her last dollars on food to supplement what she could scavenge, ducking through the streets trying to look dangerous the rest of the time. She'd forgotten how to talk to people. "He's hurt. I think he's sick, too."

"You'd better come inside," Dr. Kozlowski said. Jones found herself inside and in a bright little examining room in what seemed like four or five steps. She kept her eye on the door.

"What's your name?" the veterinarian asked the dog, noting the voder collar. She was stripping off the suit with sure, efficient hands.

The dog lay panting and didn't answer. "Ah-geez," Jones said.

The vet looked surprised. "How do you spell that?"

"I haven't any idea," Jones said. She stood by the examining-room door, calculating the fastest way out of the building.

"He's not your dog, is he? Did you find him?"

Jones wouldn't give her any clues. She shoved her hands in her pockets and waited, glancing at the door.

"You did a good job, keeping him warm. This must hurt him, here." Dr. Kozlowski examined the wound with gentle fingers. "I'll give him a shot of antibiotic[1] and clean this up, and then we should be able to sew it back where it belongs." She shook her head, looking at the damage. "I'll need to find his owner."

Jones had been waiting for a moment when the vet was distracted, to make her dash, but when she heard this she cried, "No!"

The vet frowned. "No?" Her fingers moved across Ah-geez's dirty fur, pulling it this way and that like an outfielder looking for a softball in tall grass. "Ah. This dog has been hit," she said to herself. "There, there. Another scar there. Oh yes. Creep."

"You'll take care of him?" Jones asked. *Oh, please,* she thought. *Don't send him back.*

"This dog has been hit, and I don't think he's been fed enough. And he's still a puppy. No, I don't think I'll be sending him back where he came from," Dr. Kozlowski said. "We'll take care of him." She was preparing a needle now.

"I can't pay you," Jones said.

"Don't worry about that," said the vet. "I'm on the animal-protection board. I'm their consulting veterinarian. We do that. You did a good thing, bringing Ah-geez—Ah-geez?—here."

"Um. Thanks." The vet was putting the needle under the dog's skin; Ah-geez twitched. Jones inched toward the chair over which the vet had draped her heatsuit.

"Jones help," said the dog in its thin voder voice. "Jones hurt help." Jones was stealthily lifting her suit from the chair. She froze.

"Your friend?" the woman said. "Yes, she helped you."

"Jones," the computer voice said insistently "Jones Jones Jones hurt Jones hurt. Jones hurt help cry. Bad master hit Jones Jones asleep cry. Cry asleep cry bad master."

She had not! Jones thought, flushing. She'd been awake all night, watching over Ah-geez. She thought. Anyway, maybe she had night-mares about—all that. A long time ago. But she didn't cry in her sleep, not ever, not asleep or awake. She couldn't afford to let anyone know what the tears were about.

Not even a dog. But she must have fallen asleep from exhaustion with-out realizing it, so exhausted she talked in her sleep. The vet would figure out she was a runaway, and then—

1 **antibiotic:** a medicine that kills harmful microorganisms

The door was very far away. She had to get out before everything fell apart.

The vet was cleaning the wound, and she didn't look at Jones. She said, in the same calm voice in which she'd talked about antibiotics and stitches, "Sometimes when a dog gets hit enough, he thinks anyone he sees is going to hit him." The vet touched the dog's torn flesh quickly but gently, sponging it clean. "Rotten thing. Most people who hit dogs don't bring them to me, but I see them too often anyway."

Jones was almost to the door. *Squeeze out through it and run until you can't run anymore,* she told herself. It was the only plan she could think of.

"So then there's a dog thinks everyone is going to hit him. But not everyone hits dogs." She looked then, at Jones, who was stuck in the doorway as though it were only inches wide. "You didn't." Then she said, "If you're brave, and you find the right person, they won't send you back to anyone who hurts you."

"Help Jones help good Jones good help," said the dog. He looked up at the vet and the vet nodded at him, as though she understood everything, though she couldn't possibly.

Jones was dismayed when she felt tears standing in her eyes, embarrassed when Dr. Kozlowski put a hand on her shoulder and walked her gently back inside. "It will help your friend," the vet said in a matter-of-fact way, "if you stroke his head so he knows he has a friend here while I'm sewing this up."

So that's what Jones did. ❧

SCREAM OF THE LITTLE BIRD

DAVID S. JACKSON

It takes a special kind of courage to stand up against your friends and neighbors—especially if you're a member of Alaska's proud Eyak Indian tribe. But that's what Glen ("Dune") Lankard, 39, had to do to help preserve the last remaining coastal temperate rain forest in North America.

The opportunity was born of a disaster, the 1989 *Exxon Valdez* oil spill. After Exxon agreed to pay a $1 billion settlement, environmentalists had a great idea: Why not have the U.S. and Alaska governments use the funds to buy development rights to some of the 44 million acres of land held by native Alaskans? Then tracts could be set aside as protected forests. Native Alaskans could invest the proceeds, and forests would be saved for hunting, fishing and tourism. But the natives would have to forgo income from logging. Advocates of the plan needed a native Alaskan to help sell it, so Rick Steiner, a University of Alaska biologist, and David Grimes, a fisherman from the village of Cordova, recruited Dune Lankard.

At the time, Lankard was a commercial fisherman who sat on the board of the Eyak Corp., which administered the tribe's land rights. He had grown up fishing for salmon and herring in Cordova and never identified with environmentalists. "I used to call them 'granolas,'"[1] he says with a laugh. But he had become concerned about how runoff from logging operations was polluting the streams fish use to spawn.

---

1 **granolas:** term for a cereal made of rolled oats that is also used to refer to people interested in health food, fitness, ecology, and/or a hippie lifestyle

When he first proposed the idea of forest protection to the Eyak Corp., his fellow board members voted him down, 8 to 1. "They called me a greenie and a tree hugger," he recalls. Undeterred, Lankard gave up his fishing business, set up the Eyak Rainforest Preservation Fund and began lobbying politicians and native Alaskans throughout the state. "Indigenous people have thousands of years of being preservationists,"[2] he would argue. "We need to become stewards of the land again." In Lankard's view, not only the trees and streams were endangered; so were the native cultures that depended on them. But he was taunted on the street and cursed at sea. An Indian logger pushed him against a wall in a Cordova bar and threatened him with a pool cue. He was voted off the Eyak Corp. board and sued twice.

Lankard took his fight all the way to Washington, where lawmakers would oversee the land deals. He became a familiar sight in the Capitol with his battered leather backpack, laptop computer and a small, smooth stone from his beloved Copper River that he always carried. The chief of the Eyak tribe renamed him Jamachakih. Translation: "little bird that screams really loud and won't shut up."

The lobbying finally paid off as other native Alaskans warmed to conservation. By 1998, nearly 700,000 acres of coastal habitat from Kodiak Island to Prince William Sound were protected, giving a windfall of $380 million to the native corporations.

Dune Lankard

Now Lankard wants to stop the building of a road across the Copper River Delta Basin, a rugged wetland where bald eagles still soar. "This is the last refuge," says Lankard. "Our way of life is gone if they build that road." His opponents had better prepare for a long battle. ∾

---

2 **preservationists:** people who preserve and protect the environment

Blue Diamond

Neal Shusterman

Quiet Saturday evening. My parents took my sister to the movies so I can slave away in peace at the kitchen table. TV off. Stereo shut down. Quiet Saturday evening. Until Quinn comes by.

"Dude, you're gonna study yourself to death," says Quinn.

I turn a page in my algebra book. "Math midterm on Monday," I tell him. "My parents are gonna be ticked if I don't pull down a decent grade."

Quinn shakes his head, grimacing, as if the mere thought of studying was something horrific. "They ride you too hard, Doug."

"It's all right," I tell him. "I'll get 'em back by getting into some super-expensive Ivy League school[1] they'll have to take out a mortgage to pay for."

He shrugs at that. We're both finishing up our junior year of high school, but I get the feeling he's not college bound—which is weird, because his whole family has degrees coming out of their ears. Parents, sisters, brothers—he's the fifth kid in his family—which is why they named him Quinn.

Quinn flings open the refrigerator, and looks for something to plunder. But my Dad's on a diet, which means that the proverbial cupboard is bare, not to mention the fridge. We all lose weight when Dad's on a diet, whether we want to or not.

Quinn closes the refrigerator hard enough to dislodge a magnet or two. "How can you study without brain food?" He asks. "Whadaya say we go get something to eat."

---

1 **Ivy League School:** an old and exclusive college in the northeastern United States

"Gotta study," I tell him, trying my best to focus on the list of equations on the page.

"So, bring your book with you."

I can see Quinn's having one of his "What-about-me" moments. He's bored, he's got nothing to do, and so the whole world has to put down whatever it happens to be doing just to entertain Quinn. I know he won't leave me alone until he gets his way, and I figure I could do with a short break. I mark my place in the textbook as I close it, fully believing that I'll get back to it later that night. Call me an optimist. Or call me a moron.

▲ ▲ ▲

Quinn drives his dad's new Lexus. His dad *never* lets Quinn drive the Lexus—he even locks the steering wheel with "The Car Club" just to keep Quinn away from it.

So much for antitheft devices. Quinn weaves skillfully through traffic on Harbor Boulevard. He drives kind of the same way he walks through crowds—suddenly, skillfully darting to the left or right to avoid people and objects in his way as if his whole life is just the negotiation of a maze. I've gotta admit, it's a trip being in his wake. You never quite know what off-the-wall thing he's going to do next. Me, I'm about as predictable as a traffic light—which is probably why we've been such good friends since grade school. He keeps me from turning into a drone, and I keep him from sailing off into the stratosphere. It's what we call in science a "symbiotic" relationship.

A thin crescent moon shines through the sun roof, cold and sharp as a scythe. Before us the Boulevard lights fly by, as we talk about girls, sports, and global warming . . . and then I notice that we've passed all the usual fast-food places. I ask Quinn what gives.

"I don't feel like the usual stuff tonight. I need a place with atmosphere," he says. "Let's go to Planet Hollywood—I'll buy."

Before I can answer, he pulls across four lanes, to make a well-orchestrated, but totally maniacal left turn. I glance at the little airbag symbol on the dashboard in front of me, for reassurance. "Well, okay . . . if you're buying."

As we speed down the freeway, it occurs to me that Quinn has never offered to buy. He even used to make his dates pay for their meals until I convinced him that that was sick and twisted. I begin to wonder if, perhaps, he's gotten a part-time job or something, so that now he can squander his own money instead of just his parents'.

We miss the turnoff for Planet Hollywood. From my window I can see its neon globe orbiting past us.

"Nice one, Quinn." And I begin to feel a bit edgier than usual. Perhaps because Quinn didn't even try to fly across a million lanes of traffic to make the exit at the last second. Instead he just held the wheel steady, staring forward with an unreadable expression on his face.

"It's okay," he says. "Actually I think there's another one."

"Where?"

"Just down the road a bit."

But I know of no other Planet Hollywood nearby. "Where down the road?"

He hesitates a moment, then he finally says, "Las Vegas."

It hits me slowly, like a kick to the groin. It takes a few moments until I get the full impact. This is not a study break, this is a road trip, at the worst possible time, in the worst possible way.

"No!" I tell him flatly. "No, Quinn, you're not going to do this! It's crazy, even for you."

But he only grins, and I know that he had planned this all along.

"I'm getting out," I threaten.

"So get out," he says, but makes no move to slow down the car. Then, in what must be a flash of sinister inspiration, he picks up the car phone, and leaves a message for my parents. "I've kidnapped Doug for his own good," Quinn says into the phone. "He'll be back sometime tomorrow. 'Bye."

Realizing that my algebra book is in the trunk, inaccessible until Quinn chooses to stop the car, I bring my hands to my face as if covering my eyes can make this all go away. Well, all right, I have to admit, beneath the layers of worry, there's a small part of me that's excited —after all I've never been to Las Vegas . . . but the thing is, I know Quinn well enough to know that he's lying. This trip isn't for my own good—it's got something to do with him. This is more than his usual restlessness. A four-hundred-mile road trip isn't powered by boredom and nervous energy. There's something else squirreling around through his head.

"You know, your parents are gonna kill you." I tell him.

"Not if I do the job first," he says.

For a moment I wonder what possessed him to say that, but then he cranks up the stereo, and it blows any thoughts I have out through the open sun roof.

▲   ▲   ▲

Desert night, loud and glaring. A massive black pyramid to our left, probably larger than the real ones, and the sprawling emerald cathedral of the MGM Grand to our right. Quinn pulls into the valet, like some high roller.

"Are you supposed to tip the valet on the way in or on the way out?" He asks me, as if I have any idea, then says "Who cares?" and gives the valet five bucks without a second thought. I notice there's a whole wad of bills in his usually empty wallet.

"What, did some old relative die and leave you a fortune?"

"Been saving up," was all he says, then he hands me a fifty. "Here," he said. "For the casino. You'll owe me."

"Yeah, like forever," I say, but I keep the fifty anyway, shoving good old Grant[2] deep into my pocket.

---

2 **Grant:** President Ulysses Grant, whose picture appears on $50 bills

Terrified that I'll get thrown into some seedy Las Vegas jail for being underage,[3] I move cautiously through the MGM casino. In a hidden corner, I dump some change into a slot machine. Three lion's heads on my first pull. Ultimate beginner's luck. *Ching-ching-ching-ching-ching.* Two machines down, a pasty, painted old woman with a cigarette glued to her lip grunts in disapproval. I collect my winnings, and seek out Quinn, who has just found a suitable blackjack table. In certain light, Quinn could pass for twenty-one . . . but this isn't the light. The second he sits down, the pit boss[4] asks him for identification.

Quinn wastes no time. He does one of his evasive maneuvers, and we exit stage left from this particular MGM production.

The story's the same beneath the ivory ramparts of Excaliber, and the miniaturized skyscrapers of New York New York. ID talks; snot noses walk.

Quinn's face begins to narrow into a frustrated scowl as we get back into the car. Actually, I'm figuring this is a good thing, because how much money can you lose if no one lets you play?

. . . But leave it to Quinn to find some rundown dive where no one seems to know the difference between seventeen and twenty-one—not even the blackjack dealers.

We sit beside a drunk construction cowboy, at a stained blackjack table, five-dollar minimum. Seems like adding cards is as close as I'll come to algebra tonight.

I win, Quinn loses. Big. An hour later, I walk off with two hundred bucks, not to mention the bulge of coins still in my pocket, and Quinn's wallet is empty.

And yet he doesn't seem to care. He heads toward a cash machine in the corner, and swipes a credit card through. His mother's card. About now I begin to feel guilty. After all, I'm supposed to be Quinn's safety net, right? I shouldn't have let him blow all his cash at that table. The thing is, I was having too good a time watching them take away his chips, and pile up mine. I grab his hand before he can enter the credit card's PIN number.

"Hey Quinn, maybe you should—"

But he shakes my hand off of him. Not just shakes it, but hurls it. Violently. "Just leave me alone, I know what I'm doing."

3 **underage:** younger than the legal age for gambling

4 **pit boss:** the person who oversees games such as blackjack and poker

He enters the number, and punches in two hundred dollars. I can't believe it. "What's wrong with you? Your parents'll ground you off the face of the earth!"

"Yeah, but I won't be on the face of the earth."

Long silence as I try to fathom what he's trying to tell me.

"What's that supposed to mean?"

He plucks the money from the machine, and gages his own answer before saying it out loud. "Exactly what you think it means," he says. "And if you don't believe me check the glove compartment."

▲   ▲   ▲

Half an hour later we're back in the car. I had watched, feeling helpless and useless as Quinn threw chips randomly down on a roulette table. All two hundred dollars gone in thirty minutes. I don't know what to think. I don't know what weird head game Quinn is pulling, and why he chose tonight to pull it.

What he said—maybe it's just a joke, I think. He's always dredging up practical jokes, from the pit of his eccentric soul and sometimes they go too far. Like the time he staged that car accident on April Fools' Day, when all the victims, before the angry eyes of police and paramedics, jumped up and started singing the National Anthem. But it was an unspoken rule that Quinn never pulled jokes on me.

He continues driving down the Strip. Not weaving the way he usually drives, but patient with the impossible traffic, as if he's in no hurry to get anywhere in particular.

Again I look to the little airbag emblem on the dashboard in front of me . . . and then to the little release button just beneath it.

The glove compartment.

Before I lose my nerve, I reach out, push the button, and the little door pops open to reveal the car registration in one corner, and in the other corner a small black revolver. This is not April Fools'. I shudder and slam the glove compartment closed so I don't have to see it anymore. Quinn just stares ahead.

"So roulette's not good enough for you?" I force out. "Now you have to play Russian Roulette?"[5]

Quinn shakes his head. "Naah. All the chambers are loaded."

5 **Russian Roulette:** a dangerous game in which players load one cartridge into a revolver, point the muzzle at their own heads, and pull the trigger

I don't bother to look. I believe him, although I wish I didn't. Of all the things I want to do and say, only one makes it to the surface. "Why . . . ?"

He shrugs it off like it's little more than cutting class. "It's just something I have to do." He glances at me almost grinning. "Lighten up—it's not like I'm gonna do it right in front of you or anything. Hell, I might not even use the thing, if I come up with a better way."

"So why am I here? Am I supposed to come up with your 'better way'? Because you can forget it."

"Don't be dumb. You're here because I can't have a good time in Las Vegas alone, and I'm gonna have a damn good time tonight. So let's just keep having fun. Okay?"

"Yeah. Yeah sure." I say, wondering what part of this he defines as fun. I want to talk to him. I want to start some conversation that will somehow get me into that brain of his so I can decipher what's going on in there. But all I can say is, "Where are we going now?"

He points up ahead, where a slender white tower rises more than a hundred stories up off the Strip. "The Stratosphere Tower," he says. "I hear it's a real trip!"

▲ ▲ ▲

A thousand and eighty feet in the air, we ride a roller coaster that flies around the top of the Stratosphere, threatening to eject its passengers into an unpleasant sky dive. When I was ten, it was Quinn who taught me that roller coasters are much more fun when your hands are up in the wind . . . but today I grip the safety bar tight, and watch Quinn hurling up his hands, daring the ride to send him flying. He's a roller coaster himself—maybe that's why he likes them so much. There's times when he's flying on so much energy, you can't help but be caught up in whatever he's doing. Then there are the times he's so down on everything you just want to shove him under a rock until he has something pleasant to say. Sometimes when it's really bad he disappears for a few days into his room.

So, he's manic-depressive.[6] I know that, I'm not an idiot. But no matter what he thinks, it's not a reason to blow his own brains out.

The coaster rolls around the tower again, and as I watch Quinn, it occurs to me the real reason why he brought me here. It wasn't just to keep him company, whether he knows it or not.

6 **manic-depressive:** a psychological condition in which people feel at times wildly excited and at times very depressed

After the ride, we stand together on the observation deck, the air remarkably still for this height. It's two in the morning, and the city below shines as bright as day. Quinn glances up at the guard railing. He tests the fence with his hands. I know what he's thinking.

"Hey listen," I say, "once you've aced[7] yourself, do you think I could have your CD collection?"

He snaps his eyes to me, caught completely off guard by the request. Then he shrugs. "Sure, I guess."

"Good. You don't mind if I sell the ones I don't like, do you?"

7 **aced:** slang for "killed"

He lets go of the fence. "You're gonna break up my collection?"

"Face it, Quinn—nobody in the world is gonna want some of those weird groups you've got."

"They're great groups!" he insists.

"Yeah—and you know what?" I lean a bit closer to him. "You're never going to hear a single one of them ever again."

I can see the thought beginning a little volley in his head.

"What's that group you like so much? 'Blanco Bronco'? Didn't you say they have a new album coming out this month?"

"Next month."

I raise an eyebrow. "Tough break."

It's not like his resolve really wavers. It's just that I had thrown something new into the equation. Granted, it was a small thing, but still he has to factor it in—and when it comes to factoring equations, studying or not, I could wipe the floor with Quinn.

"Nice try," he says to me with steely eyes. Then he heads inside without looking back at the fence.

▲   ▲   ▲

Four A.M. We sit in Circus, watching a bad Country-Western group perform in a lounge for a crowd of five. We don't order any drinks, so no one bothers to kick us out. I squirm silently, nervously, trying to think of a million ways to stop him. Meanwhile, Quinn's looking more and more withdrawn, as he feels his own time running down. Did he think he could fit a whole lifetime into a twelve-hour spree?

He takes a deep breath after the most godawful song. "Gotta use the bathroom," he says. He gets up, and, since I'm feeling exhaustion set in, I don't go with him.

Then about twenty seconds after he leaves, I realize he might not be going to the bathroom at all. How could I be so stupid!

Panicked, I stumble over the cocktail table, and race off to find the bathrooms, praying that he's in there for the usual reasons.

I fly into the bathroom, and my heart sinks. He's not there. There's just a fat man in a plaid jacket drying his hands with one of those electric hand dryers. "Don't you hate these things," the man says to me.

A stall opens and out steps Quinn. He looks at the way I'm huffing and puffing like I just ran the hundred-meter. He can only meet my eyes for an instant before looking away as he washes his hands. "What's your problem?"

"Just don't do that again," I tell him. "Don't just walk off."

He doesn't answer me.

"C'mon," he says, "Nothing left here." He dries his hands on his pants, and strolls out. I match his pace, not following in his wake anymore, but walking alongside him. It's easy to do that, now that he's moving straight, no longer darting in and out. Now I realize that, in spite of all pretensions, today isn't one of his manic days. He's not depressed either. He's somewhere in between. I guess that in-between can be just as dangerous.

The Lexus is parked in a bleak parking garage. The place is desolate, with half its lights burned out. I make sure he lets me in first, so he can't get in and leave me there to go do his final business alone.

He puts the key in the ignition, but turns it just far enough to get power to the windows, which he rolls down, letting in the chilly night air. He doesn't turn on the engine. Instead he just watches the keychain swing back and forth, until it comes to rest.

"So what now?" I dare to ask.

He still won't look at me. I can hear the cartilage gulp of his Adam's apple as he swallows. "This is harder than I thought."

"You know I won't let you go through with it."

"You can't follow me into every bathroom."

It's a truth that hits home, and this time it's me that has to look away.

Quinn takes the keys out of the ignition, and fiddles with them for a moment, buying time by connecting each key to some lock four hundred miles away.

"Sometimes," he begins, "sometimes the world feels like this black hole, and I'm just sort of skating around the edge. There's lots of times I feel like I'm falling in." And then finally he looks at me. "Unless you've been there, you can't imagine how awful it feels."

I could try to console him by telling him that I have been there, but the truth is, I haven't—and maybe he's right. Maybe I can't imagine that.

"Anyway," he says, "I never want to be there again."

He takes a quick glance at the glove compartment, and then back at me. Yeah, I know why he had me come on this trip. He needs me to stop him—to be his safety net for the biggest drop of all. But what can I say to him that will make that black place any less real? I could try to convince him what an awful world this would be without him . . . after all we've both seen *It's a Wonderful Life,* right? But in the here-and-now that just doesn't ring true. The world would not be worse off without him. It wouldn't be better off either. It would just . . . be.

A car comes screeching around a bend in the parking garage seizing our attention. It's an old beat-up car. Big one. Some Cadillac relic from the seventies. It screeches to a halt. Inside are two guys that look like they're straight from a post office mug shot. It is the classic prelude to a mugging. Or a murder.

The bald driver peers at us with rheumy bovine[8] eyes, and the stringy-haired guy riding shotgun leans way out of his window, shouting at Quinn through our open window.

"Hey, buddy, wanna buy a diamond."

Quinn is caught entirely off guard. His jaw bobs up and down, but says nothing. He fumbles to get the key back into the ignition, but before he can, the guy is out of the Cadillac and leaning into the window, with a little velvet bag.

"See, I won it playing poker the other day," he tells us. "But I owe big bucks to bad people, if you know what I mean. They won't take the diamond—they want cash . . . I gotta get some now."

He tilts the bag, and out rolls a perfect blue diamond. At least three carats. It glitters even in the dim lights of the garage. "It's worth a few thousand, but I'll take whatever I can get."

"No thanks," says Quinn. Again he reaches to turn the ignition. I'm not exactly sure what comes over me in the instant. Perhaps it's that look of terror on Quinn's face. I want that look to stay—just long enough to snap him back away from the edge he's been talking about.

"Wait a minute," I say, pulling the keys from the ignition. "I want to see the diamond."

The stringy-haired guy throws Quinn the evilest evil eye I'd ever seen. "I'm going to talk to your friend," he says, then comes around to the other side of the car.

"What are you, nuts?" Quinn whispers to me. "Are you totally insane?"

"You betcha!" I whisper back.

The guy shoves his hand through my window and lets me examine the diamond. "I'm desperate, man. What'll you give me for it. A thousand? Eight hundred?"

I grab my wallet and pull out the two hundred I won.

---

8 **rheumy:** watery; **bovine:** cowlike

The guy starts to looked seriously distressed. "Aw c'mon! Two hundred? This is the real thing here—see?" Then he takes the diamond and drags a broad stroke right across the windshield. It leaves a foot-long scar in the glass. "See? Only a diamond can do that!"

Quinn just looked at the scratch in horrific disbelief. "He scratched the windshield with a diamond," he mutters. "My father's gonna kill me."

I hold out my wad of bills to the scuzzy guy. "Two hundred. It's all I've got. Take it or leave it."

He gives me an evil eye, but not quite as evil as the one he gave Quinn. "Fine. Give me the money." I hand him the cash, and he gives me the diamond. "There. If you got a girlfriend it'll make her real happy . . . and if you don't it'll get you one."

Then he hops back into the Caddy with his cow-faced friend, and they blast into hyperspace once more, leaving Quinn and me alone with one blue diamond.

I give Quinn back the keys, and he starts the car, speeding us out of the lonely garage, and into the bright lights of the predawn strip.

I roll the diamond around in my fingers, watching how it catches the colorful lights around us.

"You're crazy!" announces Quinn. "Those guys could have killed us!"

Of course he's right. It was a stupid, impulsive thing for me to do. But there was a victory in that. For both of us.

"We had a revolver to defend ourselves," I remind him.

"Oh, yeah, that's real smart. Pull out the revolver and get blown away by sawed-off shotguns."

I have to smile at Quinn's reaction. Usually it's me chiding him for being a grade-A lunatic. It's good, for once, to see it turned around. And it's even better to see him heading toward the interstate. It means there's one thing I know he won't be doing tonight.

"You don't really believe that guy's story do you?" Quinn asks. "I mean, the diamond's probably stolen, or it's a fake."

"Probably."

"So what did you buy it for."

"I didn't buy it for me, I bought it for you." I toss the diamond into his lap. He swerves a bit as he tries to retrieve it from the seat.

"What are you talking about?"

"If the guy's story is for real, then you've got yourself one hell of a diamond," I tell him. "If it's stolen, I'll bet there's a reward when you turn it in—and if it's a fake, big deal. It wasn't my money I gave him anyway—

it was the casino's." Then I smile. "You gotta be just a little bit curious about it. When we get home, you should take it to a jeweler and get it checked out."

Quinn throws me a resigned glance, that also seems tinged with gratitude as well. Not for the diamond . . . but for the fact that I've managed to head him home. As we merge on the interstate, I turn to see dawn break over the palaces of Las Vegas, lights still burning, refusing to be outdone by the rising sun.

"This stupid diamond isn't much of a reason, you know," says Quinn. "Tomorrow, I'm gonna be back in the same place."

"Blanco Bronco," I remind him. "You gotta hang around to hear their new album next month. Promise me that much."

I can practically hear Quinn adding time to his personal clock, like coins to a parking meter. "And then what?"

"Isn't your sister due in a few months?" I suggest. "You're gonna be an uncle. Promise me you'll be here long enough to be an uncle."

Quinn shakes his head. "It's all little reasons. Don't you get it, I can't find any big reasons."

"Maybe there *are* no big reasons. Maybe people stay alive because there's seventy years' worth of little reasons all lined up one after another." And then I ask him again. "So promise me you'll be here to be an uncle."

He thinks about it for a long moment, then nods decisively. Another coin in the meter. "Yeah. Okay. I can promise that."

Then he becomes quiet and darkly pensive. I begin to worry about the things that might be going through his mind . . . until he says, "My parents are gonna go nuts on me when I get home."

We both think about that, and, strangely enough we begin to laugh, because that seems so microscopically unimportant now. In a few moments, we're caught in an uncontrollable fit of giggles—the kind that comes when you've been awake for twenty-four hours.

"I can't wait to see the look on my dad's face," says Quinn, "when he sees that diamond scratch on the windshield!"

And we lose it again, laughing until our sides begin to ache . . . because now getting back home—both the good and the bad of it—has become something to look forward to. ∾

RESPONDING TO CLUSTER TWO

WHAT WOULD YOU DO FOR A FRIEND?

Thinking Skill   ANALYZING

1. What are three ways in which roommates Helie and Stephanie work at their friendship in "Kimchee and Corn Bread"?

2. In "Jones and the Stray," what does Jones risk to help Ah-geez? Why does she take these risks?

3. **Analyze** the characters in this cluster. In your opinion, who does the most for a friend? Be prepared to discuss your response. You might want to use a chart such as the one below to record your ideas.

Character	What this character does for a friend
Helie	
Stephanie	
Jones	
Ah-geez	
Dune Lankard	
Doug	
Quinn	

4. Two of the pieces in this cluster are fiction: "Jones and the Stray" and "Blue Diamond"; two are nonfiction: "Kimchee and Corn Bread" and "Scream of the Little Bird." With a partner, come up with three differences between fiction and nonfiction based on these selections.

5. **Foreshadowing** is a technique authors use to hint at future developments in a story. Find three examples of foreshadowing in "Blue Diamond."

Writing Activity: Analyzing the Risks of Friendship

In all of the selections in this cluster, the main characters take risks or make sacrifices to save a friendship. After analyzing the risks these characters take, come up with a list of three things you would <u>not</u> do for a friend. You may want to use the chart in Question 3 to prepare your response.

A Strong Evaluation

• states the purpose of the analysis
• demonstrates careful examination of each part of the topic
• supports each point with evidence
• ends with a summary of the ideas presented

CLUSTER THREE

Friend or Enemy?

Thinking Skill EVALUATING

SHAKING

ROBERT MORGAN

For us a handshake was a duel:
two boys in a friendly clasp
of greeting were fighting a test
of power. Who squeezed first might have
an advantage, unless the cold
tendons got strained, and the grip,
so big and cruel, at once would
weaken from the quick exertion
as the other built up a grasp
that overrode and then melted
the opposing hand, while we both
kept grinning hello. But the best
defense was to cup your palm so
knuckles weren't aligned for grinding
but curled under the hostile force.
It was the feint[1] of giving in,
while the rival bore down and thought
himself near victory, that was
the last strategy. And when he

crunched you toward acquiescence[2] and
withdrawal from the lethal shake,
you put everything, your whole weight
and blood and warmth and thought, pumped down
through wrist and elbow and shoulder
on the opponent's paw as his
smile registered in surprise and pain
and you broke down his control in
the vise of your own gesture of
reciprocation,[3] serious welcome.

1 **feint:** trick
2 **acquiescence:** submission
3 **reciprocation:** giving back

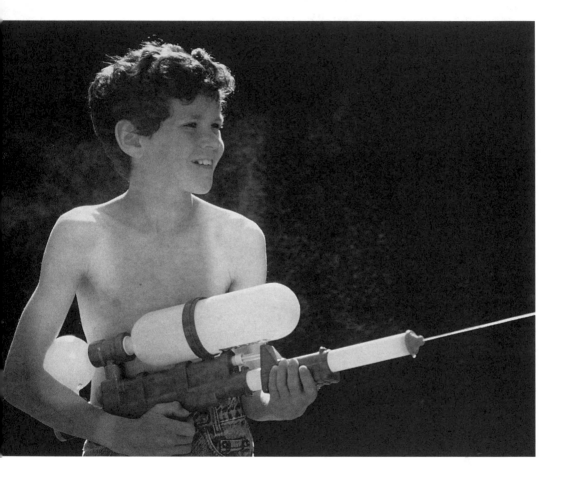

WAR GAME

NANCY WERLIN

What I did to Lije. It might have seemed . . . okay, in some ways it *was* cruel; I'll give you that. But I had to do it. It was important. Okay?

You don't see? Fine. I'll explain.

Lije—Elijah Schooler—and I were friends, though nobody knew it except him and me. It had just kind of worked out that way over the years, with Lije being a boy and two years younger and going to the private school his father paid for. His bedroom window faced mine over three feet of alley, and he used to sleep with the light on. Sometimes at night we'd talk for hours—or rather I would—when Lije was worried and had trouble sleeping. For years we did that. And he lent me books. His school had an incredible library, and he could get me anything I wanted.

It wasn't a big secret, our friendship. It was a little secret, something pleasant, but not really important. Until last August when I was fourteen.

It'd been an almost unbearably hot summer. At first it was just the little kids who had the guns—you know, the big plastic machine guns with huge tanks for water. Super-Soakers. Water Uzis. Ricky Leone and Curt Quillian and even Curt's little sister, Janey, were jumping out from alleys and from around corners and behind cars, screaming like police sirens and soaking everybody in sight. The rest of us had to defend ourselves. Before you knew it, nearly every kid in the neighborhood between six and fourteen had a water gun. They were under fifteen dollars at the supermarket.

They were just plain fun, the guns. I'd had no idea. Though I'd seen real guns before, around the neighborhood and at school and stuff, I'd actually never had a toy gun before, even when I was little. But I felt so powerful, cradling the gun under my arm and pumping away. Every time you hit someone, they'd yowl. Run. Unless they were armed too; then they'd whip around and shoot back. It was incredible. I'm not a violent person—none of us were, really (except maybe Lina at times). We weren't gang kids; in fact, we did our best to keep away from the gangs. It was the city. It was summer. It was hot. That's all.

At first, we big kids just did like the little kids and ambushed each other. But then I said something, and we got more ambitious. Kevin DiFranco and Lina Oswego organized two teams—armies—and we were all assigned ranks. The little kids were privates and scouts, and the older kids were lieutenants or spies. I was a lieutenant colonel and head of the war council. "You're smart, Jo," Kevin said. "You do the strategy." Of course Kevin and Lina made themselves generals. Within a week, there were nearly thirty of us involved.

At first I just did it for something to do. And maybe also because it felt good to get the attention from Kevin. He'd never had much to do with me before. I wasn't interested in him, you understand; I wasn't interested in any real boys right then. That was the summer I had the tremendous crush on Talleyrand, and in all my fantasies I (or rather, my alter ego,[1] Anne Fourier) was deeply involved in the politics of the French Revolution. Anne generally disguised herself as Pierre-Ange Gaultier, a boy journalist and the best of Talleyrand's spies. I had worked out nine separate and extremely elaborate scenarios, all of them leading to the danger- and passion-filled moment in which Talleyrand would realize he was in love with Anne. But where were Anne's loyalties? With him or with the Revolution or with only herself? It depended on how I was feeling that day. Usually in the end I was on my own side, though, because in a war that's how you survive. That's how Talleyrand did it.

Kevin DiFranco was both popular and cute, but he couldn't have competed with my fantasy world if he'd tried.

But my imaginary life was private—I wouldn't even have told Lije the details, and he borrowed most of my books for me. A massive crush on a centuries-dead Machiavellian[2] priest-politician in a powdered wig wasn't the kind of thing you shared. And if I'd gone on to tell people about my mental war games, my elaborately researched historical alter ego, well,

---

1 **alter ego:** a second self who is either a trusted friend or an opposite side of one's own usual personality

2 **Machiavellian:** term used to describe a person who follows the philosophy of Machiavelli, who believed conduct in politics was marked by trickery

my facade[3] of social respectability would have cracked right there, and I'd have been the butt of a million idiotic jokes. If you want to survive, you have to blend in.

Plus, even I couldn't live in the eighteenth century all the time. And our real-life war game fascinated me. I had a lot of say in it, a lot of control. I was the one who said we were the opposing guerrilla factions of a country in the throes of civil war, a country located right on the equator, full of steaming jungles (the playground and the abandoned factory lot around the corner on Eastern Avenue). The jungles, I said, entirely surrounded the bombed-out capital city (our street and its alleys). I was the one who set up the POW camp behind the brick wall in the truck yard, and I wrote up the rules surrounding[4] capture, punishment, and death. Kevin and Lina were the generals, okay, and they planned the raids and battles and took care of the daily details. But I was the one who designed the game. You could even say it was *my* game.

It was amazing, when you thought about it, when you saw how well it worked. I mean, it had never happened before—all the kids in the neighborhood hanging out and doing something together. We were all different ages, of course, and on top of that there were cliques. But it worked. For a few weeks, it worked. And we had such fun.

Only Lije wasn't playing. He didn't have the summer off from school; he was in some special enrichment program and came trotting home every afternoon at around three o'clock and let himself into his apartment with his key. He'd be there alone until after eight o'clock, because his mother worked as a secretary for some big downtown law firm, and she didn't get home until late. And of course his father was, as the social workers say, not in the picture. Actually, Lije had never met him. But he did pay the tuition for Lije's private school, and, hey, I've heard of worse absentee-father deals. Mine, for instance. Lije hated it, though. Hated him. It was a funny thing. Lije was a fat, scared mess with a runny nose, and he couldn't sleep without the light on. But underneath that he was okay. Because he could hate.

We were on the second day of a two-day truce (really an excuse to concentrate on covert ops[5] and training) on the afternoon we all noticed Lije. He had just come out of the convenience store on the corner of

3 **facade:** outward appearance

4 **surrounding:** concerning

5 **covert ops:** secret operations

Eastern Avenue and Tenth Street. He looked dorky, especially considering the heat, in his long pants and cheap dress shirt and school tie and with his backpack dragging his shoulders down. He was holding a wrapped ice-cream sandwich that he'd obviously just bought, and he was completely absorbed in trying to pick open the wrapping.

He was a perfect target, and Lina pounced. "Ambush!" she yelled, and in seconds her SWAT team had him surrounded. Lije looked up, blinking, at the four Super-Soakers leveled at his head.

"Hand over the ice cream," Lina said, "or you're dead."

Lije shot a glance at me, where I was lounging on a stoop with Kevin and a couple of the little kids. But then his eyes skimmed on past. Right then it hit me that we had never talked to each other in public, only from our windows across the alley. Out here on the street, that relationship was nonexistent. It didn't even need saying. So I grinned at Lije but didn't move or speak.

Silently, he handed over the ice cream to Lina. She laughed, made a gesture, and the SWAT team opened fire. Lije didn't move. He stood there and took it, until the tanks were empty and he was completely soaked.

We all laughed. "Feels good, huh?" Lina said. If you knew her, you'd know she was actually being friendly. For Lina.

And that was the moment I understood that Lije wasn't okay after all; that he would need help to be okay. Because he wouldn't just laugh too. Couldn't even force himself to do it; couldn't even pretend. Instead, he acted like a jerk; minded; showed he minded. Why didn't he know better than to show it? Why did he have to let his lip tremble and his face get red? Why did he run like that? Why did he let them—let us—let me—see he was scared?

It's dangerous to show your fear. It marks you as a victim. And watching Lije run away like a little kid, I was afraid for him. And right then I knew I had to do something to help him. I just didn't know what, or when.

That night, though, was completely ordinary. Lije's light came on well before the sun set, and I leaned out of my window and called his name.

"You all right?" I said.

"Yeah." His hair was wet; he'd obviously just taken a shower. Another shower.

"Sorry about today," I said casually. "You just have to laugh, you know. You can't let it get to you." I watched him carefully to see if he understood what I was saying.

Lije shrugged. "Jerks," he said. He said it like he meant it, but I saw his chin tremble and his eyes brim. So he didn't get it. I decided to leave it for now.

"Did that book I wanted come in from interlibrary loan?"

He nodded and handed over a hardback copy of J. F. Bernard's biography of Talleyrand. Inches thick, crammed full of detail, and with plates not only of the man himself, but also of his wife and some of his more famous mistresses. I was thrilled. "Thanks tons," I said to Lije. "This is great. How long can I keep it?"

"Two weeks." Now that we were back on familiar ground, he was feeling more comfortable. He leaned on the windowsill. "Jo, listen. I think the librarian is getting suspicious. She asked me if I had finished the books I already had out."

"What'd you say?"

"Oh, I just shrugged and said I was working on it. But then she started asking me what I found so interesting about France, and was I taking French, and stuff like that, so I had to get out of there fast. You know, I'm not supposed to take out books for other people."

This wasn't news to me. Why was he suddenly making such a big deal out of it? "Look," I said, "I'd get them myself if the public library still did interlibrary loan."

"I know. I just want to be careful and not get into any trouble."

"Don't worry about it," I said. "They won't know anything you don't tell them. It's in your control. You're in charge."

"You always say that," Lije said, which was true. But I'd always thought before that he heard me. I looked at him and saw that he had that rabbity look that he got when he was tense, brooding about his father, or about his mother and money, or something. Life was rougher for Lije than it should have been, just because he took everything so hard, so seriously. He didn't know how to protect himself at all. I wondered how I'd missed that before.

So I said, "Okay. I'll tell you some stuff you can dazzle the librarian with." And even though I wanted nothing more than to be alone with the new book, instead I climbed up onto the sill and leaned against the window frame, while Lije pulled up a chair to his window and propped his chin on his hands. I told him about the bread riots and how they guillotined the rich creeps and how, for the greater good, Charlotte Corday—what a woman, huh?—stabbed Marat to death in his bath. And as I talked, softly as I always did when I told Lije stories, the sun set, and if it hadn't been for the smog and the city lights, there might have been stars.

"You tired enough to sleep now, Lije?" I asked finally, long after midnight. It never got quiet in our neighborhood, not exactly, but most people were sleeping.

He didn't answer, and for a moment I thought he was already asleep. Then he said, "Jo?"

"Yeah?"

"You like me, Jo, don't you? You're my friend?"

He'd never asked me anything like that before. I said, "Is this about today?" Lije didn't answer, but he did look at me, his cheeks all pudgy and his eyes, well . . . suspicious. I said, "I already told you I was sorry that happened. But Lije, you took it too seriously, you know what I mean?" But he was still staring at me with that odd look on his face, *needing,* and so finally I said, "Yeah. Yes, Lije. I like you. I am your friend. I've always been your friend." Which was the truth.

"Good," Lije said. "I'm your friend too, Jo. Always."

And then he stood up and leaned out the window and reached his hand across the alley. He held out his arm, suspended, for a few moments before I realized he wanted me to take it and shake hands. I did that. I think . . . now I think it may have been the only time we ever touched.

Then he went to bed, and I read about Talleyrand until dawn, when my mother came home from her night shift and made me get some sleep.

The next day it was nearly noon by the time I finally got outside, and Kevin was ticked at me for missing morning council. Worse, our planned morning kidnapping of Lina's best sniper, Ricky Leone, hadn't worked; instead Ricky had shot two of our guys, and by our rules—my rules—they were dead for the rest of the day. An hour later Janey got caught spying and ended up in the POW camp. Lina was triumphant, Kevin furious. There were about fifteen of us engaged in a huge argument about the rules, with me trying to cool them off and Lina nearly purple with rage.

And that was when Lije came down the street again, looking dorkier than ever. I saw him see us standing there, armed of course; saw his eyes dart around as if looking for a hole to dive into. But then—because he really did have something underneath, like I said before—he squared his shoulders and came on anyway, marching like a windup toy soldier, looking neither left nor right. Hostility, fear, anger—they were almost visible, pulsing in the air around him as he tried to push his way right through us.

Kevin stuck out his foot and tripped him. Lije fell onto his hands and knees. A few of the littler kids snickered. Lina laughed, and it wasn't the friendly (for Lina) laugh of yesterday. She'd picked up on Lije's hostility, of course, and taken it as disrespect. "You looking for trouble?" she said to Lije's back. Two of her kids stepped forward and leveled their guns at Lije, grinning. "Soak him?" one said.

It was addressed to Lina, but Kevin answered: "Go ahead." Kevin hadn't even finished talking when Lina's kids opened fire on Lije.

First just those two. But then more of them, in a circle around Lije, shooting down first at Lije's back. Then somebody—Lina?—kicked Lije viciously, forcing him over. And the rest of the water reservoirs pummeled down on his face and chest. He was pinned to concrete by the force of the water.

Talleyrand—master strategist and supreme survivor—always knew how to improvise on the moment. He would have been proud of me, because I knew immediately that this was the moment to help Lije. I didn't even have to think how to do it. I knew.

I waited until everyone else was done. Waited until Lije got up, slowly. His palms were scraped and bleeding. He didn't say anything. He looked at me. And it was that look, the one I'd seen on his face last night. *Help me,* it said. *Protect me. Be my friend. I can't do it alone.* But he didn't say anything, he just watched me. Waited.

I emptied my own gun into his face. Then I said, "Run on home, kid. You don't belong out here. You might get hurt."

After a few more excruciating seconds, Lije left, dripping.

That night, I lay alone in bed watching the light in Lije's window and reliving those minutes. I waited until after it was full dark. Then I went to the open window and called his name. I didn't really think he would come, but he did. He looked terrible.

"Give me back my books," he said. It was what I was expecting. It still hurt, though. Inside, I felt the way he looked. But I didn't show it. I handed him the Talleyrand biography—at least I'd had one night with it—and the others he'd got me before. I wondered how I'd get books now. Somehow. I'd figured something out.

"You're going to be okay, Lije," I said evenly.

Lije shook his head. He was standing awkwardly, arms tense, hands dangling out of sight below the windowsill. "You lied to me," he said.

I shrugged. Stared right back at him as his arms bent and lifted. I saw with pride that he had his own Super-Soaker now. He aimed it at me. His aim was lousy because he was crying, shaking, and so most of the water missed me, but I stood there and took it, as he had, until his reservoir was as empty as mine.

"I hate you, Jo," Lije said. "You're not my friend."

He went back into his room. I went and got a towel and dried myself. Then I waited. And after a while Lije put his light out and, to show me that he could, for the first time slept—if he did sleep that night—in the dark.

Okay, *yes,* I was sorry to hurt him. But the French have a saying about things like this. *C'est la guerre.* Literally it means "that's war," but really it means "that's life." And . . . Lije doesn't understand. Not now. But you can. He was wrong about my not being his friend.

I am the best friend he will ever have. ∾

Take Your Best Shot

Jackie Vivelo

Willis Strum was shot during a brief skirmish on March 12, 1864. With a dozen other Confederates, Willis had been caught by a small band of Union soldiers. He had been hit twice and left for dead on the brown, wet leaves under an oak. For a little while, even Willis wasn't sure whether he was dead or alive.

After a bit, he opened his eyes and saw sunlight playing through oak leaves. He had done nothing more than think about moving and test a muscle or two before he knew he couldn't go anywhere without help. He was weak from shock and loss of blood and he'd also had a bone broken by a musketball. But Willis was just nineteen and not so worn down by sickness and short rations as most of the Southern troops were in that spring of '64. He'd be all right if help came soon enough.

He dozed for a time. When he opened his eyes, the sun was directly overhead. Light caught a single drop of water ready to fall from the point of a leaf and, to Willis's eyes, transformed the drop into a small marble globe that burned with an inner life.

"It's my shooter!" Willis cried, and he wasn't referring to his gun.

The light of the sun directly above him seemed to spread into a rainbow-colored circle and then to break into a hundred different colored dots.

March was usually the time for their first marble games of the year, played in a ten-foot circle on a dry patch of Virginia earth. Instead of fading in the sunlight, the sight of that circle was becoming sharper for Willis. He and Bucky Webber had put their best marbles into the ring, thirteen marbles; mibs and hoodles they called them.

"Bucky'll win," somebody said.

Willis was good too, but somehow everybody always favored Bucky.

The two of them knelt at the pitch line, a line drawn outside the big circle with its center touching the circle, and lagged for the right to shoot first. The lag line was drawn on the opposite side of the circle, also just outside with its center touching the circle. Lagging just meant shooting to come as close to the lag line as possible; the one who shot closest would go first.

"Wait a minute!" Jimmy Johnson cried. "I'm saying Bucky will win. Play him for keepers, Bucky. You can get that blue mib away from him."

"We don't play for keeps," Willis objected. "We only play for fair."

But the circle of watchers had decided they wanted the excitement of a game played for "keeps," instead of for "fair," in which case marbles are returned to their owners.

Bucky joined them. "Come on, Willis. For keeps this time."

Willis closed his eyes against the sight of the ring of bright marbles. Closing his eyes was a mistake. It pulled him back into the present where he was dizzy and hurt and weak. He opened his eyes and focused once more on the marble shoot.

They had been eleven that spring, he and Bucky and Jimmy Johnson, a year marked in memory because Bucky and his family had moved away that summer.

He could see all the marbles, clear against sky and tree branches above him. Playing for keeps! If he had known, he wouldn't have put out that sky-blue mib. There were two others out there that he didn't want to lose; one was a special shade of green like the first leaf of summer and one was mixed red and gold. They were out there now. He couldn't take them back. And he'd just sound like a coward if he insisted on playing for fair when Bucky and everybody else wanted the game played for keeps. Willis thought that for him it would be enough to win. He wasn't interested in taking Bucky's hoodles and mibs, but he didn't argue. He just eyed the lag line and gave it his best shot. Then Bucky shot.

"Bucky's closer," someone in the little crowd of onlookers called.

But Bucky said, "Measure it."

Willis was closer and had the right to go first. How was he supposed to have a chance to win when everybody was rooting for Bucky?

Willis took his shooting position, carefully chose his spot, and then knuckled down. One knuckle had to touch ground right up to the moment the shooter left the hand.

"No h'isting!" Jimmy Johnson warned.

Willis ignored him; he knew enough to keep his hand down.

"No hunchin'!" Bucky laughed to show his advice was a joke.

Willis's eyes moved over the ring, estimating distance, choosing a target, aiming. Knuckle down, hand steady so it couldn't hunch forward, he shot. Bucky's black agate marble, his "aggie," was propelled from the ring. Willis reclaimed his shooter, took aim again and this time bagged his own green marble. In rapid succession he took two more of Bucky's marbles. He now had four marbles. To win he needed three more. He took aim, but the shooter slipped from his fingers before he was ready.

"Slip!" he called and reached to retrieve the shooter for a second try.

"No slip!"

"That was no slip!" the watchers called.

"If it doesn't go more than ten inches, it's a slip," Bucky intervened. "Let's measure it."

"I'll measure it," Jimmy said and pounced on the shooter sending it flying out the other side of the circle. "Anyway, it was more'n ten inches."

"Yeah, ten inches at least," somebody else said.

Willis didn't mind giving up his turn when he lost it fair, but he didn't like being cheated out of it. Now there was no way to prove a slip. He picked up his shooter and moved back to let Bucky have a turn.

One—two—three, Bucky shot straight and picked up three marbles in a row, two of his own and one of Willis's. He took aim at Willis's mib with the snow swirls in it. It spun clear of the ring. He took aim at the red and gold marble Willis thought of as "fireball." The shooter hit it hard and took it out of the ring. Two more and the game would be Bucky's.

"Atta boy, Bucky."

"Knuckle down."

Bucky aimed and made a square hit on the sixth marble in a row.

Willis thought Bucky was a sure winner. A cloud over the sun cast the ring of marbles into darkness. For a moment Willis knew again that in reality he was lying on the forest floor with his life's blood slowly draining away. Time was passing. Help wasn't coming.

The shadow shifted and the ring of marbles reappeared. Willis saw that Mary Ellen had pushed through to the front of the circle of watchers. Hers was the shadow that had fallen over the ring.

Bucky looked up at her too, but Mary Ellen kept her eyes on the three marbles still lying inside the circle. She looked very solemn.

Bucky knuckled down, took aim, and fired his shooter into the ring. It missed. Without a word, he picked up the shooter and moved out of the way.

Willis shut out everything else. He could still win if he'd just concentrate. He settled his shooter just right on the curl of his index finger, hit it with his thumb and saw it take out a marble. He now had five marbles.

He fired again and collected his sixth marble. A stir went through the spectators. Willis and Bucky now each had six marbles. Only Willis's blue mib was left in the ring. If Willis missed this shot, Bucky would win for

sure. Willis didn't care so much about winning any more. But he cared about that sky-blue mib. And he cared about Mary Ellen. Of course, Bucky did too. Her showing up like that was probably why Bucky missed his seventh shot. No, Willis didn't care so much about winning, but he hated to lose in front of Mary Ellen.

Now there was just one marble left. If it wasn't Willis's on this shot, it would be Bucky's.

A jostling for position ran through the spectators.

"No hunchin'!"

"Don't h'ist it now."

Willis lifted his head and for a wonder Mary Ellen met his eyes. For a long moment, he saw her eyes as blue as the sky-blue mib he stood to lose.

Somebody said, "Knuckle down, Willis."

But Mary Ellen didn't say anything.

"Get it, Willis!"

Somebody was rooting for him after all. Mary Ellen's solemn face eased into a smile, and Willis knew that the voice in the crowd wasn't the only one on his side.

And Bucky saw the smile too. He moved forward, clapped Willis on the shoulder, and said, "Take your best shot, Willis!"

And Willis did.

The shooter seemed to move in slow motion. It made solid contact with the last marble and the marble sailed toward the edge of the ring.

For him to win, it had to go out and the shooter must leave the ring too. If the shooter stayed inside the ring on this last shot, that final marble would be put back and Bucky would get another turn.

The marble rolled over the ring and away. And the shooter followed it. Willis had won.

"Good shot!" Bucky said and sounded as if he meant it.

Willis carried his marbles in a leather drawstring bag. He took them out and counted them several dozen times that spring, over and over, admiring their colors and the way they caught the light. He played and lost and played and won. But in each game he put aside the marbles he had won from Bucky so he couldn't lose them to someone else who might want to play for keeps.

When Bucky came to say he and his family were moving away, Willis knew he'd lost his best friend. The night before the Webbers were supposed to leave, Willis wrote a note that said, "I didn't want to play for keeps." He tied it to his leather bag of marbles, with all the marbles inside, and left it by Bucky's front door.

The first thing next morning he went back again to say goodbye. He was too late. Everybody was gone and Willis had never been sure Bucky had gotten the marbles.

He wished he could see old Bucky now. He'd like to tell him that when you're dying you don't always relive your whole life, that the one thing he'd relived was that marble game. Bucky would know which one.

▲ ▲ ▲

Through light and gloom, horses approached, and someone shouted, "There's ten or a dozen Rebs here. Check 'em for survivors!"

Willis opened eyelids that were heavier now. The ring of marbles, bright as the sun, was blotted out once more. Only this time it wasn't Mary Ellen's face between him and the light. It was somebody in blue who was holding his bayonet poised above Willis.

To the sun-haloed face, Willis said, "It's your turn, Bucky. Take your best shot."

A dumbfounded Union corporal deflected the force of his blow and sent his bayonet into the ground.

"We'll take this one in," he said to the man beside him.

"Begging your pardon, Corporal, but the colonel said no more wounded prisoners. We ain't got the beds for 'em."

"We've got a bed for this one. He's an old friend." Then speaking just to himself, Corporal Webber added, "Though how he knew me behind this beard and him delirious, I sure don't know."

▲ ▲ ▲

Later, when Corporal William Webber stooped beside a camp bed in a tent full of sick and wounded prisoners, Willis asked, "Why'd you spare me? This is supposed to be a war, y'know."

"Yeah, I reckon it is," Bucky said, "but it wasn't my idea to play for keeps." ❧

DIRECTIONS TO THE ARMORER

ELDER OLSON

All right, armorer,[1]
Make me a sword—
Not too sharp,
A bit hard to draw,
And of cardboard, preferably.
On second thought, stick
An eraser on the handle.
Somehow I always
Clobber the wrong guy.

Make me a shield with
Easy-to-change
Insignia. I'm often
A little vague
As to which side I'm on,
What battle I'm in.
And listen, make it
A trifle flimsy,
Not too hard to pierce.
I'm not absolutely sure
I want to win.
Make the armor itself
As tough as possible,

1 **armorer:** maker of weapons and armor

But on a reverse
Principle: don't
Worry about its
Saving my hide;
Just fix it to give me
Some sort of protection—
Any sort of protection—
From a possible enemy
Inside.

HEY, JEALOUSY

Francesca Delbanco

The week before winter break, I drove my best friend Janine home from school every day. She'd applied early to Stanford, and waiting to hear whether she had been accepted was making her crazy. I'd try to distract her during the drive, blabbing on about what we should do for New Year's Eve (three years in Ron Weiner's basement seemed like enough). But once my Toyota turned onto Orchard Street and her mailbox came into sight, it was no use. I'd tell her how smart, how deserving, how phenomenally cool she was—that it would be Stanford's loss if she didn't get in. But day after day, there was no word.

Then, on a Thursday, it came: a thick first-class package with crests all over it. We ran into Janine's house to tell her parents, whose excitement made it seem as if she'd been elected President. They opened champagne and called the grandparents. I hung around until Janine's boyfriend came over with red and white roses. Then I headed home to study calculus. For those of us who hadn't applied early to college, grades still counted.

The next day Janine was a school celebrity. Everybody said they'd known all along. Not that it took a crystal ball: She was Earth Awareness president, field hockey team captain, a homeless shelter volunteer. You could almost see the halo glowing over her head. These were the reasons why I admired her. She deserved her success.

That's what I told myself, anyway, as Janine got interviewed by the school paper. Yup, that's my pal Supergirl. Yup, I'm sure tickled that she's getting all this recognition. Yup, 100 percent thrilled. Overjoyed. That's me.

The smile plastered on my face was not convincing. But admitting that I was jealous felt as mature as admitting that I wet my bed (yeah, right). I figured that everybody in our class was feeling a twinge of Wish it were me—but what I was feeling for Janine was something more like Wish it weren't you.

I confess, this was not my first brush with the green-eyed monster. The Esprit chambray jumper Liz Cook wore on the first day of fifth grade is still emblazoned on my memory, down to the red-bandanna trim. But that was a back-to-school outfit, and being envious of your friend's dress is more forgivable than being envious of her life.

I thought about revealing my true sentiments to Janine. But what would I say? "I can't stand it that you're the center of attention. Your accomplishments make me ill. P.S. Do not forget that I scored higher on the SATs"? That wasn't my style. So I let it lie.

I'd resisted the urge to throw a temper tantrum on the floor—when a few days later, I was smacked with another outrageous injustice. After breaking down and declaring the Ron Weiner Basement Fête[1] my New Year's Eve destination of choice, I got a call from my friend Tristanne—on the morning of the big night—so excited, she was hyperventilating.

"Dave Spiegel invited me over tonight to watch the beginning of a movie he's directing," she announced.

This was only the most beautiful guy ever to walk the halls of Greenhills School. He'd graduated two years before us and was studying filmmaking at New York University.

"He's home for break?" I asked, stunned. "Shouldn't he be in, like, Cannes or something?"

"He's here. I ran into him at 7-Eleven. I can't believe he remembered me."

I pictured a split-screen image of where we'd each be at midnight. "Is it going to be just you two?"

"I think so. We got into this really intense conversation about documentary filmmaking, and he said he'd love to show me his work. Can you believe? Come over now and help me choose what to wear!"

Yeah, I thought, I'm seeing a tiara, sequins, maybe a mink stole. Go ahead and borrow mine.

I looked down at my sweatpants and flannel shirt. The prospect of making a dent in Tristanne's bed while watching her layer on lip gloss

---

1 **fête:** a large, elaborate party

seemed pretty grim. "I'm sorry, but I promised my mom I'd help her clean up before her dinner party tonight."

No, I wasn't going to let thoughts of our hometown Quentin Tarantino and his adoring sidekick ruin my time at Ron's. Hey, the place was rocking. But then, as we grooved to the live-via-satellite broadcast of Don Henley in Times Square, Ron noticed that Tristanne hadn't come.

"She's at Dave Spiegel's," I said. The room got all quiet. Suddenly everybody was listening to me.

"How did that happen?" Ron asked.

"Apparently they ran into each other at 7-Eleven."

"And he asked her out?"

"Sure. She must have looked gorgeous by the light of the Slurpee machine." Egged on by the snickering, I kept going. "You know Tristanne and her pretentious art-appreciation shtick. Thank God it finally worked—maybe tonight she'll get the first kiss she's been gunning for since sixth grade."

As the yolk dripped off my face, I realized what I'd done: I'd announced Tristanne's most guarded secret to our whole gang. Was that me? It seemed so. Janine, who five minutes before had been jamming with me to "Dancing Queen," was looking at me like I'd sprouted horns and a bright-red tail.

That entire night I felt bad. Bad that I was toasting the New Year with a can of Coke; bad about the kind of friend I was. You're supposed to want the best for people you love, and while I'd (kind of) hidden my bitterness in Janine's case, with Tristanne I was acting like a character from *Heathers*.[2]

After the party I drove alone over to Tristanne's house. A light was on in her room. Even though it was late, I knocked at the kitchen door, and she came downstairs to let me in. She was glowing. I heard the story from start to finish—how they ate three bags of microwave popcorn; how she didn't even notice when it was midnight, because Dave was talking about some camera he had used to shoot his movie; how they listened to three Elvis Costello CDs. Very John Hughes,[3] down to the goodnight kiss in the middle of the street.

2 ***Heathers***: a movie about vain, shallow teenaged girls

3 **John Hughes**: director of '80s movies about young people such as *The Breakfast Club* and *Pretty in Pink*

And even though part of me cringed while I smiled—okay, most of me, between my jealousy and my fear that she'd find out about what I'd said at the party—I knew I was acting like the kind of friend I wanted to be.

Maybe that seems like faking it. It kind of is. But sometimes, at least where I come from, that's the best you can do. For all I know, there are people who always feel psyched when great stuff happens to their friends, but I haven't figured out how to be one of them. Honestly, I don't even feel that bad—it's part of me and it's not going to change any time soon.

Sometime after that awful night I realized that getting jealous isn't immature; what is is letting jealousy make you mean. You can't train yourself not to feel something, but you can train yourself to let it go before it turns you all snipey. So at times my congratulatory grin is a little strained—but it's there. And I know I'll be glad when I win the lottery and all my friends have to clap. ∾

Farewell, My Friend

Roger Ebert

For the first five years that we knew each other, Gene Siskel and I hardly spoke. Then it seemed like we never stopped. We began as film critics for the two morning papers in Chicago, both still in our 20s and eager to establish ourselves—preferably at each other's expense. When we were asked to work together on a TV show, we both said we'd rather do it with someone else. Anyone else.

At first the relationship on TV was edgy and uncomfortable. Our newspaper rivalry was always in the air between us. Gene liked to tell about the time he was taking a nap under a conference table at the television station, overheard a telephone conversation I was having with an editor, and scooped me on the story. I got scooped more than once; it really hurt in 1997 when he sat down to talk about the movies with President Clinton.

He considered himself a reporter as well as a critic, and he was one of the best I ever knew. It was typical of Gene that when he got interested in the Bulls, it wasn't just as a fan, but as an expert; he knew as much about the Bulls as most of the sportswriters who covered them. It was consistent with his reporter's orientation that some of his favorite films were documentaries such as "Hoop Dreams."

After his surgery last May, his first public appearance was at a Bulls game. It was important to him that he be there. And it was typical of Gene's determination that he returned to the job as soon as he could. Two weeks after his surgery, he was watching movies on tape in his hospital room and phoning in his reviews to "Siskel & Ebert." Soon he was back in the show's balcony, and in print at the *Tribune* and *TV Guide*, and on the air at CBS.

Someone else might have taken a leave of absence then and there but Gene worked as long as he could. Being a film critic was important to him. He liked to refer to his job as "the national dream beat," and say that in reviewing movies he was covering what people hoped for.

Because the movies could do such a powerful job of reaching into the minds and emotions of audiences, he took it personally when they disappointed him—when they were lazy and stupid. He told me about a proud moment as a father: He asked one of his daughters how she'd liked a movie and she told him that, well, she didn't. "Some kids think they're supposed to be polite and just say they liked a film," he said, "but I've always told my children it's important to make up your own mind."

He was ferociously honest in his opinions. He didn't care about seeming fashionable. When he picked "Babe: Pig in the City" as the best movie of 1998, some people thought it was a strange choice. I didn't. The movie was on my top 10 list too, and I knew why Gene admired it: It was original, it was trying to do something new, it had been overlooked in the flood of more mainstream product, and it had something worthwhile to say. It stood for what he stood for.

When Gene saw a movie he really admired, he almost glowed. Toward the end of the screening of "Fargo," he walked over to me in the dark and whispered, "This is why I go to the movies." When he saw a movie he hated, he liked to suggest that filmmakers ask themselves this question: "Is my film more interesting than a documentary of the same actors having lunch together?"

Gene kept private about the state of his health in the months after his surgery. I understood why. He wanted to protect his family from the attention that might result. He wanted the focus to remain on his film criticism. And although it was obvious sometimes that he walked slowly and was in pain, I never once heard him complain. He carried on with a bravery that is hard to imagine.

We did the TV show together for 24 years. It was a strange format: two ordinary-looking guys from Chicago, sitting in a balcony talking about the movies. One question we were asked, again and again, was: "Do you really hate each other?" There were days at the beginning of our relationship when the honest answer sometimes was "yes." It was unnatural for two men to be rivals six days of the week and sit down together on the seventh. But over the years respect grew between us, and it deepened into friendship and love. ∾

Gene Siskel (left)
and Roger Ebert

Responding to Cluster Three

Friend or Enemy?

Thinking Skill EVALUATING

1. In the poem "Shaking," the friendly ritual of handshaking is shown to sometimes disguise competition, tension, or hostility. In what other ways do friends sometimes hide competitive or unfriendly feelings behind a friendly face?

2. **Evaluate** the friendships in this cluster. A year after the selection ends, who will be friends and who will be enemies? Explain why. You may want to use a chart such as the one below.

Selection	Friends or Enemies?	Reasons
Shaking		
War Game		
Take Your Best Shot		
hey, jealousy		

3. In your opinion, does Jo act as a friend or an enemy when she refuses to come to Lije's aid? Explain your response.

4. In the poem "Directions to the Armorer," the speaker arms himself not against others but against his own self. In what ways can people be their own worst enemies?

5. Using "hey, jealousy" as a starting point, identify some unexpected outcomes of jealousy.

Writing Activity: Evaluating Friendship

Evaluate the selections in this cluster and your own experience with friendship. In your opinion, is it easier to make a friend or an enemy? Write a persuasive essay on your choice in which you use examples from the selections and your own experience to support your opinion.

A Strong Persuasive Essay

• begins with a statement of the writer's opinion

• uses facts, quotes, examples, and so forth to support the opinion

• is organized for maximum impact, often with the most persuasive arguments presented last

• presents information clearly and logically

• concludes by restating the writer's opinion

CLUSTER FOUR

Thinking On Your Own

Thinking Skill SYNTHESIZING

BUILDING BRIDGES

ANDREA DAVIS PINKNEY

At first, Mama Lil said it plain and simple: "No."

Then, like always, she spoke her full mind. "Bebe, get that backward idea out your head. That grit-work[1] ain't no place for you. And besides, I ain't never heard of no girls to be doing *that*. You need to be getting yourself a real summer job, something civilized."

We'd just finished Sunday breakfast. Mama Lil had fried up a batch of Dunbar's ham, the meat we ate only on Sundays, holidays, and special occasions— my all-time favorite.

Mama Lil pushed her breakfast plate aside and centered her ashtray. She took a final drag on her cigarette. Through the haze of smoke that clouded her small, tight face, she spoke slow and deliberate. "And don't ask me again about signing that permission paper," she said. "I ain't gonna be the one who allows you to take part in such foolishness."

I leaned back in my kitchen chair, my arms folded tight. The chair's vinyl stuck to the skin on my shoulders, taping itself to the place where my T-shirt scooped down at my back. It was as if, like Mama Lil, that chair wanted to hold me in its clutches.

I'd been living with Mama Lil since I was six, when my own mama and daddy were taken by the Walcott apartment building fire. Lillian Jones was my mom's mother. Everybody on our street called my grandmother Mama Lil, and that's what I called her, too. She was a mama to everybody, it seemed, always scolding the other neighborhood kids about playing their music too loudly in the street, or hanging out too long

---

1 **grit-work:** slang for dirty, physically demanding work

on the front stoop of our house. Mama Lil and I had been butting heads ever since I could remember. And the older I got, the more at odds we were.

Mama Lil hated the six studs I wore in my left ear; I hated the tacky red wig she pulled down close to her eyebrows whenever her hair wasn't done.

She thought I weighed too much and dressed badly; I thought she smoked too much and overdid it with her fake gold chains. Time after time, she'd ask me, "How you ever gonna land a decent man with them chunky arms and those hoochie-cut[2] T-shirts that put your navel on parade? No self-respecting seventeen-year-old should be letting it all hang out like that."

Whenever Mama Lil got on her "self-respecting seventeen-year-old" sermon, I came back with a warning under my breath: "When some homey[3] *tries* to snatch all that shiny tin off your seventy-three-year-old neck, don't come crying to me."

If Mama Lil really wanted to heap it on, she'd start nagging me about my hair. "Child," she liked to say, "them natty braids you call dreadlocks[4] look like the fright 'do of a zombie."

Yeah, over the years Mama Lil and I had thrown a lot of dissing[5] words back and forth. But then, too, I had a sister-to-sister connection to Mama Lil that not many kids had with their grandmas. I could talk to her real direct. I could tell her the deal, straight up.

Mama Lil and I didn't beat around the bush because all we had was each other. There was no time to waste on half-spoken words. I was Mama Lil's only true family, and she was the only real parent I had. If I ever left her, she'd have nobody; and if she passed on, I'd be alone in this world.

▲ ▲ ▲

For weeks I'd been asking Mama Lil to let me join the youth renovation team, a group of kids that had been chosen by city officials to work with a squad of contract engineers to help repair the Brooklyn Bridge. The project would last the summer, pay good money, and help

---

2 **hoochie-cut:** slang for clothes styled in a vulgar way

3 **homey:** slang for close friend; here it means a member of a gang

4 **dreadlocks:** a hairstyle in which the hair is worn in long ropelike locks

5 **dissing:** slang for disrespecting

me get to college, where I wanted to study engineering. The whole thing sure beat flipping Big Macs at Mickey Dee's.[6]

But Mama Lil wasn't having it. To her, I was "stooping to do a bunch of low-down mess-work." Truth be told, Mama Lil was scared of something she didn't know. She hardly ever left our neighborhood in Brooklyn; to her, the Brooklyn Bridge was a mystery.

And I think that deep down Mama Lil was afraid something bad would happen to me, the same way it happened to my mama and daddy. Also, Mama Lil couldn't read or write very well—I read most of her mail to her, and helped her sign her checks—and she hated to admit it. The two-page consent form she had to sign, giving me permission to work on the bridge project, was a challenge to her pride.

Then there was the fact that I would be the only girl working with the bridge crew. (My acceptance letter said few girls had applied; of those who did, I was the only qualified candidate, based on my grades.) Mama Lil thought it just wasn't right that I'd be working on a project staffed only with boys and men. "If God had meant you to do a man's work, he would have made you a man. It's that simple," she said.

All these strikes stood against me ever getting to work on that bridge. But the biggest obstacle of all, the thing that made Mama Lil the most stubborn, was my dream of becoming an engineer. Mama Lil didn't fully understand what an engineer was. I'd tried to explain it to her; I'd shown her my sketchbook full of drawings of city structures and machines, but Mama Lil didn't know any engineers. She'd never seen one at work.

And to make matters worse, she'd taken it upon herself to ask her friends down at Rimley's Beauty Parlor about engineering. They'd convinced her that I was headed down the wrong path. "Ain't no black woman doing no engine-ing," she'd said.

"Engin*eering*," I'd corrected.

Mama Lil said, "Whatever you call it, it's a white man's work. You ain't got no place messing with it. We should stick with our own kind, Bebe—colored women trying to cross the white man's line is asking for trouble."

In some respects, Mama Lil was right. Black folks did need to stick together, no doubt. But not in the way Mama Lil meant. And it *was* true that there weren't many black women engineers. I knew from the get-go that if I hoped to become an engineer, my road ahead would be lonely

---

6 **Mickey Dee's:** McDonald's

and hard. But I wanted to build bridges more than anything. And working on the bridge project was the first step—a step that I needed Mama Lil's help to make. A step that started right here in her tiny kitchen.

The last of Mama Lil's cigarette smoke lingered between us.

"I wish you'd lay off those Carltons," I said, pushing the smoke away with a single wave of my hand.

Mama Lil rose from the table. She took her ashtray with her. "I'm trying to quit, Bebe, you know that," she said. "Carltons have less tar, less nicotine. They're better for you," she reasoned.

"And I'm Miss America," I huffed.

At the sink, Mama Lil lit another cigarette, then started washing the dishes. "Look, missy," she scolded, "don't be taking your bad mood out on me. You get cranky every time we talk about that nasty job you want to get." Mama Lil turned her back to me and began to fill the sink with soapy water.

"It's *not* nasty," I said, my voice rising. "Selling to the crackheads is nasty. But this is good work, Mama Lil. I'd be employed by the city—by the mayor."

Mama Lil was busy lathering the greasy skillet she'd used to fry the ham. With her back to me—she had strong back muscles that showed beneath her blouse—she said, "Bebe, I don't care if you're working for the King of Siam. Hammering a bridge together is not respectable work for a young lady."

"But, Mama Lil, working on the bridge isn't just—"

"—Don't get me wrong, Bebe"—Mama Lil kept her back to me—"all those pretty pictures you draw in that tablet of yours are real nice. But, child, doing that to earn a living is a pipe dream. *White* folks can pay their bills by sitting around doodling. We just don't got it like that."

I leaned my forehead onto the heels of both my hands. The kitchen hung quiet for a moment, its only sound the scrub of Brillo scratching the ham skillet. Mama Lil cleaned in a steady, determined rhythm. With each scrub, she hunched further over the sink, giving that pan every bit of strength she had. "This damn grease is stubborn," she said, her back muscles tense with effort.

"*You're* stubborn," I spat in a low voice. But Mama Lil didn't hear me. She just kept on scrubbing.

▲　▲　▲

That evening Mama Lil dozed off in front of her little black-and-white television set. The blue cast of the TV's light danced across her face, softening its tired lines. Mama Lil wheezed out small, breathy snores. She was sinking into the kind of sleep that often kept her on the couch—TV babbling on—all night.

I locked Mama Lil safe inside the house, and, with my sketchbook tucked firm under my arm, I headed for the street. As I walked our noisy avenue, I took in the lights and people who dotted the darkness. I thought hard about Mama Lil's mule-headed words: "Ain't no black woman doing no engineering . . . trying to cross the white man's line is asking for trouble."

I walked fast and furious for blocks and blocks, the warm summer air heaving in my lungs. My armpits had grown sticky with perspiration. The hair at my temples began to crimp with sweat. Finally, I stopped under a streetlight—a streetlight that was my hiding place—on a quiet corner, just off Shore Street. I leaned into the streetlight's cold aluminum pole, letting my breath slow itself down.

Ahead, in the distance, stood the Brooklyn Bridge. This was the best spot in Brooklyn's Red Hook section for seeing the bridge. I'd come to this corner and studied the bridge a million times. And on every one of those times, I was taken with what I'd come to call Brooklyn Belle.

I never got tired of looking out at its steel girders and iron cables—at its beautiful crisscross rafters that had started out in somebody's imagination, had been put to paper, formalized in an engineer's plans, then woven together, bolt by bolt. Now Belle was a powerful giant who carried all kinds of people to all kinds of places, day after day.

At night Belle was dressed in tiny lights that spanned her limbs. On a cloudless night like this one, she was a sight like no other sight in the whole city. Jeweled in light. *Beautiful.*

My fingers had tensed into fists at my sides, fists full of strength and eagerness. I uncurled my knuckles and shook them free of their strain. Then I reached into my jacket pocket—where my consent form for the bridge project had been neatly folded for days—and pulled out my pencil. Slowly, I flipped through the pages of my sketchbook. I'd drawn Belle in the high-noon light, at sunset, on snowy days, and on foggy twilight mornings. My favorite sketches were those of Belle during rush hour, when cars and taxis danced like trinkets along her outstretched beams.

Tonight I'd draw Belle with her lighted cape. I sketched slowly at first, then faster, my pencil working with the speed of my excitement—the thrill that worked me over every time I sketched that bridge.

I was proud of my drawings (I liked to think of them as portraits), but with each page they showed a sad truth about Belle: She needed repair. She was some forty years older than Mama Lil. And as lovely as she was, she had some serious rough spots—corroded cables, rust, chipped paint, and plain old grit that had built up over the decades. That bridge renovation project needed me; and I needed it, in more ways than I could count.

The air had grown sticky, moistening the pages of my sketchbook. It was getting late. The orange glow of the streetlight above my head flickered in the blue-black night. I slid my pencil back to its pocket, and headed for home.

If I'd had a bet on it, I'd have put my money down that Mama Lil hadn't missed me one bit. She was probably snoring up a storm by now. And her TV was most likely still blipping its hues onto her face, sending its random talk-show chatter around her living room.

▲　▲　▲

A week passed. A week of Mama Lil and I not speaking about the bridge project, or the permission form that was due—signed by her—in four days, when the renovation was supposed to begin.

We talked about plenty of other things—the hell-hot summer heat, the tomatoes at Key Food, Oprah's new look—but we sidestepped talk about the bridge altogether. And with each avoidance, with each conversation about nothing at all, the Brooklyn Bridge loomed larger. It was as if Belle were sitting smack center in Mama Lil's living room, with gridlocked traffic fighting for space on her pavement. If I didn't get my consent form signed, I would forfeit my place on the project. Every time I tried to bring it up, Mama Lil twisted her lips and raised her hand. "Don't be bringing that mess in here, Bebe. There ain't no more discussing to do."

As the days passed, I grew more anxious, and more angry at Mama Lil's attitude. On the Saturday night before the project was to start, Mama Lil did something that got me real mad. She brought home a summer job application from Rimley's Beauty Parlor, where she and her gossipy friends spent their days.

As Mama Lil lifted the application from her purse, she had the nerve to say, "Bebe, I went and done you a big favor." I gave Mama Lil a hard sideways stare.

She kept on talking. "Vernice Rimley needs somebody to sweep hair and clean her sinks. She can't pay you nothing to start, but you'd get a heap of training. By next summer you'd be doing perms and manicures, and getting tips on top of a regular salary. And you could even bring your paper tablet, so you can draw during your breaks."

Mama Lil put the application down on the coffee table between us. As she spoke, she tapped it with her finger, emphasizing her words. "Bebe, if you put your mind to it, you could be awfully good at doing hair. Give it a chance, child," she urged.

My forehead and upper lip grew moist with the sweat that anger brings on. I wiped the back of my hand across my mouth, feeling my words jump to my throat before I spoke them.

Mama Lil lit a Carlton. She sat back on her sofa, blowing smoke straight ahead. Her eyes avoided mine. "Mama Lil," I began, "*look* at me."

But Mama Lil was sinking deeper into her stubbornness. She leaned her head back, inhaled on her cigarette, and closed her eyes to release another stream of smoke. "I'm enjoying my cig, Bebe," she said. "It tastes better with my eyes closed."

I leaned in the doorway, my anger rising. "Mama Lil, your eyes are *always* closed. *Closed* to seeing me." Mama Lil's lips curled around the tip of her Carlton, letting the cigarette dangle for a moment.

I said, "I don't want to spend my summer sweeping hair. The bridge is where my heart's at, Mama Lil."

Mama Lil shifted on her couch pillow. I could see her eyes roaming beneath their lids. She took another drag, a heavy one this time, and blew out a long, quick breath. She was doing her best to tune me out. "Yeah, that's right," I said, my voice strained with frustration, "blow me away. Try to make me and my dreams disappear, like your puffs of smoke!" I was hollering now, full out. I kicked the doorjamb with the toe of my sneaker. "Damn!"

Mama Lil opened her eyes in search of the cat-shaped ashtray she kept on her coffee table. She tapped her ashes into the cat's face, then aligned her gaze with mine. Her eyes looked weary, her expression pained. She set her Carlton along the cat's ceramic tail and let it smolder. She sighed. "Bebe, I'm an old woman. I ain't got much to look forward to in this life—not many of my own dreams to go after." Mama Lil's voice trailed off to silence. Then her face softened, and for the first time ever, I saw Mama Lil's eyes fill with regret. "What little bit of dreaming I got left in me," she said, "I'm putting to you."

I licked my lips and listened. Mama Lil had more to say. "But I can't dream your dreams, Bebe. Working on that old bridge so that you can study some high-tone thing like engineering is a far-off notion that don't fit in this old woman's way."

Mama Lil let out a heavy breath. Then she admitted what we'd both known all along. "Your dreams are the kind that'll take you away from here, Bebe—away from your Mama Lil. You got big hopes, child, but they gonna leave me alone, by myself."

I shrugged.

Mama Lil said, "That's an upsetting truth, Bebe. It makes my heart hurt every time I think on it." The cigarette had burned to ash. Its smoke had gone, but its heavy odor remained in the room.

Mama Lil was right. My dreams *would* take me away from her.

I wanted to comfort her, but I wasn't willing to back out of the bridge project, or give up my plans for becoming an engineer. I knelt next to the couch cushion where Mama Lil sat and took both her hands in mine.

"Mama Lil, I got to find *my* way," I said slowly. "If that bridge renovation wasn't tapping on my soul, I'd go ahead and sweep hair down at Rimley's."

For once, Mama Lil was looking into my face, hearing my words. Her eyes were filled with sad acknowledgment.

"Let me go, Mama Lil. Let me dream," I pleaded softly.

Mama Lil sat as still as a statue. I gently pulled my hands away from hers and reached into my pocket to find the bridge project consent form. I unfolded the thick carboned papers[7] and set them on the coffee table, next to the application from Rimley's. "Mama Lil," I said carefully, "if you don't sign this—if you *won't* sign it—I'll sign it myself. I been helping you sign checks and letters for years now. I can sign your name on this consent form, and nobody'll know the difference."

Mama Lil's eyes began to dart. She looked from me to the consent form to the Rimley's application, and back to me again.

"I don't want to cross you, Mama Lil," I said, "but I will if I have to—to do what makes my soul feel right. To dream my dreams."

Mama Lil reached for her pack of Carltons, which were resting on the arm of her sofa. She felt for a cigarette, but the package was empty. I smoothed the consent form with my palm. "You want me to read you what it says?" I asked.

---

7 **carboned papers:** papers with sheets of ink inserted between them to make copies

Mama Lil shook her head. "Leave it be," she insisted. "Let me sit with it awhile."

I could feel my face growing warm again with perspiration. Night had fallen fully now, but Mama Lil's cramped living room still sweltered from the daytime heat. I could hear the boys on our block gathering to play their music on the corner. Usually Mama Lil would call from the window, hassling them to "turn that blasted noise down." But all she said was, "Bebe, get on to bed. It's getting late." I rose to my feet, hovering over Mama Lil, who, for the first time ever, looked small and sunken in her seat. "The bridge project starts tomorrow morning," I reminded her.

Mama Lil shrugged. "I know good and well when it starts, Bebe. You've told me twenty times over."

▲   ▲   ▲

That night, the night before I was to report to the bridge project, I lay awake. I was afraid Mama Lil would doze off in front of her TV and forget about the consent form. Or that the detailed instructions on the two-page sheet would frustrate her, and she wouldn't make the effort to read it through. And worse than that, I feared Mama Lil would set fire to the form with her cigarette lighter.

When I finally fell asleep, all kinds of strange dreams danced in my head: Mama Lil crossing a bridge made of Carlton cigarettes; my sketch-book filling itself with senseless scribbles; the hair from the floor of Rimley's Beauty Parlor floating up and clinging to my face, making it hard for me to breathe.

I awoke to the smell of Dunbar's ham coming from the kitchen. The sun hadn't risen; twilight slowly approached. I listened for Mama Lil's TV, but all I heard was crackling grease and the shuffle of Mama Lil's feet against the kitchen tile.

My clock said 5:36. The bridge renovation crew was scheduled to meet at 7:00 at the Tillary Street entrance to the bridge. I threw on my muscle T-shirt and jeans and grabbed my sketchbook.

When I got to the kitchen, my place was set. Mama Lil scurried between the stove and the table, setting down napkins, pouring orange juice, flipping the ham as it rustled in the skillet. She didn't even see me come into the kitchen. "Hey, Mama Lil," I said.

Mama Lil peered at me over the top of her narrow glasses, glasses she wore only for reading. Glasses that hung from the chain of one of her junk jewelry necklaces. "Sit, Bebe, your ham's ready," she said. I shrugged and slid into my chair. The sun was full in the sky, zigzagging its light across the kitchen table. The hands on the kitchen clock were settling on 6:00.

Mama Lil served both our plates. She sat down across from me and started eating. She was acting like it was any other morning, chatting on about her late-night comedy show and the pigeons that nested on the ledge of her bedroom window. I was certain she'd done away with the consent form for the bridge project, and was doing her best to ignore the whole thing.

I ate in silence, wondering if the bridge crew leader would let me onto the project without signed permission. I'd have to leave for the site soon, if I wanted to get there on time.

Mama Lil hadn't stopped talking. Now she was on to something about the high price of cornmeal.

I finished my last bite of ham, and interrupted. "Mama Lil," I said firmly, "I'm going to the bridge."

Mama Lil steadied her glasses. She took a heavy breath. "I know, Bebe," she said, nodding, "I know."

That's when Mama Lil reached into the pocket of her housedress and pulled out the consent form. "You gonna need this," she said, sliding the papers across the table.

I unfolded the form, which had become worn and crumpled. But Mama Lil hadn't signed it. It was the same as it had always been.

Mama Lil could see the upset pinching at my face. "Now hold it, Bebe," she said, "don't be so quick to put on that down-in-the-mouth expression."

"But you didn't sign the form, Mama Lil, and you know I can't—"

"Calm down, child." Mama Lil's tone was solid. She said, "You're jumping out the gate too fast."

"The project's gonna start without me!" I snapped.

Mama Lil leaned into the table toward me. Her eyes looked red-tired. Before I could speak another heated word, Mama Lil said, "I been up most the night, Bebe—thinking, praying, and trying my best to read that confounded permission paper. They sure got a whole bunch of words typed on that thing, just to say I'm gonna let you help fix a bridge."

I could feel my whole body fill with relief. Mama Lil said, "I may not know how to read that good, but I *do* know I ain't supposed to sign something I ain't fully read."

Mama Lil pushed her glasses up further on her nose. They were speckled with dots of grease that had sprung from the hot ham skillet. "Will you help me read the permission paper, Bebe?" she asked. "Will you help me understand what it's saying to me?"

I slid my chair to Mama Lil's side of the table. Together, we read the consent form, line by line. When we were done, Mama Lil took a pen from her housedress pocket. She held it awkwardly and signed the form with her crooked handwriting.

She gave her signature a good looking-over. Her face filled with satisfaction. Then she folded the form and pressed it into my hand. "Bebe, that bridge is lucky to have you," she said.

I hugged Mama Lil good and hard, then I got up to go. Just before I left the kitchen, I turned and smiled big, right at her. "Yeah, it is," I said. ∾

MOCO LIMPING

DAVID NAVA MONREAL

My dog hobbles
with a stick
of a leg that
he drags behind
him as he moves.
And I was a man
that wanted a
beautiful, noble
animal as a pet.
I wanted him
to be strong and
capture all the
attention by
the savage grace
of his gait.
I wanted him to
be the first
dog howling in
the pack.
The leader,
the brutal hunter
that broke through
the woods with
thunder.
But, instead he's
this rickety
little canine
that leaves trails

in the dirt
with his club foot.
He's the stumbler
that trips while
chasing lethargic
bees and butterflies.
It hurts me to
see him so
abnormal,
so clumsy and
stupid.
My vain heart weeps
knowing he
is mine.
But then he turns
my way and
looks at me with
eyes that cry out
with life.
He jumps at me with
his feeble paws.
I feel his warm fur
and his imperfection is forgotten.

Mike Levins
Untitled (From the 3rd Avenue El, the Bronx)
Polaroid Foundation Purchase Fund
Courtesy, Museum of Fine Arts, Boston

PROMISES

ELLEN CONFORD

This is the diary Laura gave me for my birthday. It probably didn't cost very much, but it's the thought that counts, they say. And at least she gave me something, which is more than certain people did.

I got a lot of better presents, too. Melanie gave me perfume, which my mother says I'm too young for, especially perfume named Sinful. Sarah gave me a CD of *Penny Dreadful's Greatest Hits*. I got plenty of good stuff.

So I'm not going to sit around and brood about why Tracy would do such a rotten thing to me, who has been her best friend since second grade.

I'm not going to waste my time going over and over that *extremely embarrassing* moment when I opened this gorgeously wrapped box in front of everybody. How I saved it for last because it was the biggest and looked the most expensive, and I knew it just had to be something super because no one would waste all that silver paper and blue satin ribbon and huge bow with curlicues all around on a junky gift.

I can't figure Tracy out, and I'm not even going to try. Melanie said maybe she forgot to put the present in the box, but that doesn't make sense. I mean, there's this big white box, and you wrap it and pick it up and you don't notice that it doesn't weigh anything? You don't notice that the gift that's supposed to be inside is still sitting there next to the Scotch tape and scissors?

She did it on purpose, and no matter what Melanie says, everyone at the party knew it. They couldn't stop talking about it.

Well, I'm not going to spend the next two weeks of my life, till she gets back from California, wondering why she did it, but I am definitely not going to forget that she humiliated me at my own birthday party.

I don't know what satisfaction she could have gotten out of this stunt, since she wasn't even around to see my reaction. She was on the way to the airport when she dropped off the present. Come to think of it, she didn't even seem that disappointed about missing my party.

I just figured she was excited about visiting her father. She hasn't seen him since the summer, and I know she misses him.

How could I not know? She's always moaning about it. She can be so *tedious*. You'd think she was the only kid in the world whose parents ever got divorced.

I try to make her feel better by pointing this out. "Tracy," I say, "you're not the only kid in the world whose parents are divorced. Snap out of it already. It's been a year."

And she says, "You don't understand. You never understand."

Well, I don't know what she means, since it's my shoulder she's cried on since second grade, and if I don't understand, why doesn't she find somebody else's shoulder to cry on?

Though that's easier said than done. Probably the main reason I'm Tracy's best friend is because she doesn't make friends very easily. She never did. She's the quiet type. The opposite of me.

And I'm not all touchy and supersensitive like she is. I don't make mountains out of molehills. If I had done this to *her*, she *would* sit around and brood for two weeks. She'd go over it and over it, trying to figure out how she'd hurt my feelings, or what she'd done to make me angry. She'd ask all my other friends if they knew why I was mad at her, and she wouldn't be able to think about anything else until I came home.

The least little thing upsets her.

For instance, the time I forgot about the movie we'd planned to go to.

I went to the mall that Saturday morning, and I ran into Jessica and Sarah, and we started wandering around, and then we got hungry, so we stopped at the Yogurt Hut, where this boy works that Jessica sort of likes. So we hung out there for a while, and all of a sudden I realized it was two o'clock and my mother and I were supposed to pick up Tracy at twelve-thirty.

Well, the very instant I remembered, I ran straight to the nearest phone, which wasn't even that near—I had to walk halfway through the mall to get to it—and called Tracy.

"Diane, you promised," she said. "I was looking forward to that movie all week."

"I'm sorry, Trace. I just forgot."

"You forget a lot of things," she said. "A lot of things I care about."

"Oh, come on, Tracy," I said. "It's just a movie. Don't make a huge major deal out of it."

"It's not just a movie," she said, "it's the whole—"

Then the operator cut in to say I had to deposit another dime. But I didn't see any point in staying on the phone if all Tracy wanted to do was complain about my alleged faults, so I said, "Haven't got any more change. Talk to you later."

Jessica and Sarah wanted to see the movie, so I went with them. It was really good.

Then there was last year's social studies project. Okay, that was a little more serious than a silly old movie, but still, when you think about all the truly terrible things in the world, not getting your social studies project done on time is hardly a major tragedy.

Tracy and I were partners on the project, which was due the Monday after Thanksgiving weekend. We were studying advertising claims. It was Tracy's idea, so of course she was a lot more interested in it than I was. Basically I only agreed to be her partner because I knew she didn't have a whole lot of friends to choose a partner from.

Anyway, she made a list of TV commercials and the products we would test—paper towels, toothpaste, sugarless gum, spaghetti sauce, stuff like that. She said she'd do most of the testing and that I should only do three items because I would do practically all the work on the chart and the display.

Well, it's true, I'm much more artistic than Tracy—she can hardly even draw a smiley face—but a big display like that is a whole lot of work. And even though we had four weeks for the project, Tracy only got the test results to me a week before Thanksgiving. She said she would have gotten the results to me sooner if I had done the test I said I would do, but I pointed out that since I was doing all the work on the display, it was only fair for her to do most of the tests.

"But Diane, I had to do *all* of the tests. Even though you promised to do the gum and the paper towels and the batteries. If you'd said right at the beginning you wouldn't do them—"

"I meant to do them," I told her. "I just didn't have time."

"Four weeks wasn't enough time to do three comparison tests?" she asked sarcastically.

"Some people," I said, just as sarcastically, "have more things to do with their lives than chew gum and wait for batteries to die."

"Some people," she said, "shouldn't make promises they don't mean to keep."

Well, that was totally unfair, because I didn't plan to not do the testing. It's just that a lot of other things came up, and I didn't get to it.

Anyway, even though she got me the test results at the very last minute, I had all the stuff ready to make the display—the Magic Markers, the colored pencils, the poster board. I was sure I could finish the project over the weekend.

In fact, I was already working on the chart the day after Thanksgiving when Melanie called. She was so excited I could hardly understand what she was saying.

But I was able to make out, "Uncle's ski chalet . . . Vermont . . . my folks said I could invite some friends . . . Laura and Jessica . . . real spur-of-the-moment trip . . . leaving in two hours . . . going to be so great!"

Well, I'd already started the chart, and how long could it take? We'd get home Sunday afternoon, in plenty of time to finish the display by Monday morning. Even if I had to stay up all Sunday night, it would be worth it. How could I say no?

I'd never been to a ski chalet. I'd never been to Vermont. In fact, I'd never been on skis. I knew I didn't have the right stuff to wear, but Melanie said that didn't matter. It was all going to be very country and casual, and we'd toast marshmallows in the fireplace and tromp through the snow.

She made the weekend sound like a Christmas card come to life. Nobody in their right mind would say, "Sorry, I'd really like to, but I have this social studies project to do." Was it my fault that there was a major snowstorm that paralyzed all of New England Sunday morning? I'm not God. I didn't make it snow so hard that we couldn't get out of Vermont until Monday afternoon. How could Tracy blame *me* for the weather?

And it's not my fault that Ms. Brisco is so unreasonable that she wouldn't cut us an inch of slack, even though our project was two days late because of an Act of God.

Besides, it's not as if we didn't get any credit at all for the project. We just got two grades knocked off for being two days late.

"Empty promises!" Tracy screamed. "I am really fed up with your empty promises. I can't depend on you for *anything*."

She didn't speak to me for two weeks, which was actually sort of a relief, to tell the truth. I mean, she is so self-centered. The only important problems are her problems. Nobody's interests matter as much as hers.

I don't know why I stay friends with her. I guess because I feel sorry for her, but what kind of a basis for friendship is that? And because our mothers are friends, and my mom always nags me to include Tracy in everything.

But after this rotten joke—if it is a joke—even my mother will have to admit that there's no reason to stay friends with her anymore. What possible excuse can there be for giving your best friend an empty box at her party? It would have been better if she'd just ignored my birthday completely.

No one at the party would have noticed if there was no present from her. Nobody notices Tracy anyway, and her name wouldn't have even come up this afternoon if she hadn't—

Maybe that's it. Maybe she was trying to get attention. She's always been jealous of me, I guess because she sort of fades into the woodwork when I'm around. But is it my fault that she has no personality? Can I help it if people would rather talk to me than to someone with all the spark of a stop sign?

So if I open this empty box all of a sudden, in the middle of my party, on the day of my birthday, everyone forgets about *me* and starts talking about her.

But if she's not even here to hear them talk about her, what can she get out of it? It doesn't make sense.

And I'm not going to waste one more minute thinking about it.

How could she be so ungrateful?

Not that I've ever expected her to thank me for all the things I've tried to do for her. Ha! That'll be the day.

Well, at least I won't have to pressure people to invite her places anymore, like my mother always wants me to. If it weren't for me, she'd never go anywhere at all. I can't count the number of times I've wangled an invitation for Tracy from someone who'd never include her in a party if I didn't insist.

And do you think she remembers all those times? Does she remember the parties I had to threaten not to go to unless she was invited?

Ha.

All she remembers is the one party I couldn't go to. And that was last July.

She was planning her birthday party. Of course I said I would go, even though I knew it would be incredibly boring. How could it not be boring? The other kids she invited were two girls from the school Mathletes team. We were going to eat dinner at an expensive restaurant. Her father was flying in from California.

I could just imagine the evening—her mother and father hardly talking to each other, Tracy living a ridiculous fantasy about how her party would bring them back together, and the Mathletes making witty comments about algebra.

But I said I'd go.

And I would have, even though I expected it to be the longest, dullest night of my life.

Is it my fault that Tracy tells me her party is the Saturday of July Fourth weekend, and Laura tells me her party is on July Fourth, and I say yes to both of them because I don't realize that they're the same day?

I mean, I don't walk around wearing a calendar on my wrist. It was a simple little mistake anybody could have made. If Tracy had sent me a written invitation like Laura did, I would have seen right away that her party was scheduled for July Fourth.

Laura's party certainly sounded like a lot more fun than Tracy's. It was going to be at a country club, and she invited a lot of her brother's friends, and there would be a clambake and swimming and fireworks.

"But, Diane, you promised you'd come!" Tracy shrieked into the phone when I broke the bad news.

"I'm sorry, Trace. I got my dates mixed up."

"When did you get Laura's invitation?" she demanded. "I asked you weeks ago."

"Well, that's not really the point," I said.

"It is the point," she said. "I asked you first, and you said you'd come. Now you're ditching me because you think Laura's party will be better."

"Why can't you just switch your party to another day?" I suggested. "I mean, there's only the two math nerds and us and your folks. Laura's having thirty people, and they had to rent the country club. Hey! Maybe I can get her to invite you, too!"

"My father already bought his plane ticket," she said. "It's the only day he can come. And I don't want to celebrate Laura's birthday instead of my own."

"Tracy, you won't even miss me," I said. "And you won't get any less presents, because I've already bought you a *terrific* one."

I hadn't, really, but I swore to myself that I'd buy her something extra special to make up for not going to her party.

"You think all I care about are the presents?" she yelled. "I only invited three people to my party. How could I not miss one of them?"

"I'm really, really sorry, Tracy, but it can't be helped. It's just one of those things."

"It's just one of those things that you're always doing to me," she said. Her voice was kind of tight and thin, like she had a sore throat. I hoped she wasn't going to cry.

"I said I'm sorry, Tracy. What more do you expect?"

I heard her take a deep breath. "I don't expect anything from you. Except empty promises."

"Empty prom—"

But she'd already hung up.

Laura's party was great, like I knew it would be. (And I must say I bought her a much more expensive present than this dinky old diary she gave me.) (No offense, Diary!) But her party did cost a whole lot more than mine did, so I guess it balances out.

Tracy started to hang out with the two math nerds who went to her party, and I haven't seen that much of her for the past few months.

In fact, if my mother hadn't insisted, I wouldn't have asked her to my party, and she wouldn't have given me that empty box and embarrassed me in front of all my *real* friends.

Although I'm not so sure now about how real those friends are. They've been calling all evening, saying, "Oh, wasn't that weird what Tracy did?" and "How embarrassing for you," and, "You must have done something really mean to her."

They remind me of rubberneckers staring at a car accident, full of morbid curiosity.

I'm sure the minute they hang up they call each other and gossip about me and the nasty things I must have done to Tracy.

I'll have to stop for a while now. My mother wants me to get all the party junk out of the family room.

▲　▲　▲

Well, I found Tracy's birthday card while we were cleaning up. It was in a mess of torn wrapping paper under a chair. It must have fallen off the package.

It's not even a real birthday card. There's a photograph of daisies on the front, and inside it says, "Friends are the flowers in the meadow of life." Isn't that icky?

Underneath that, Tracy wrote, "This present is just like your promises. Happy birthday."

I just looked at the card and looked at the box and wondered, *What* present? There is no present. The box was empty.

Isn't that bizarre?

Well, Tracy always was kind of weird. Who knows what goes on in her mind? I certainly don't. And I'm not going to waste one more minute of my time trying to figure it . . .

Oh. ✎

THE KAYAK

DEBBIE SPRING

The choppy waves rise and fall. I ride the wave. My kayak[1] bobs like a cork in the swirling waters of Georgian Bay.[2] I love it. I feel wild and free. The wind blows my hair into my eyes. I concentrate on my balance. *It's more difficult now.* I stop stroking with my double-bladed paddle and push my bangs from my face.

This is my special place. Out here, I feel safe and secure. My parents watch from the shore. I have on my life jacket and emergency whistle. I am one with the kayak. The blue boat is an extension of my legs. I can do anything; I can go anywhere. Totally independent. Totally in control of my life. It's so different back on shore.

I approach Cousin Island, where I have to steer around the submerged rocks. In the shallows, a school of largemouth bass darts between the weeds. A wave pushes me towards the rocks. I push off with my paddle

---

1 **kayak:** an Eskimo-style canoe that has a small opening in the center for the paddler

2 **Georgian Bay:** an inlet of Lake Huron, Canada

and I head out towards the middle of Kilcoursie Bay. Powerful swirls of wind and current toss me about.

The clouds move in, warning signs. I turn the kayak and head back to the shore. The waves peak wildly as the storm picks up. My arms ache.

I don't want to go back to shore. Nobody lets me grow up. My parents treat me like a baby. I'm sixteen, too old to be pampered.

Just off my bow, a loon preens its black mottled feathers. It sounds its piercing cry and disappears under the water. I hold my breath, waiting for it to resurface. Time slows. Finally, it reappears in the distance. I exhale.

I notice a windsurfer[3] with a flashy neon green and purple sail, gaining on me. My stomach does flip flops as he races, dangerously close. "Look out," I yell. I quickly steer out of the way. He just misses me. *Stupid kid, he's not even wearing a life jacket.* I shake my head. The boy is out of control. He's heading straight for the rocks at Cousin Island. "Drop the sail!" I call.

He does and not a second too soon. He just misses a jagged rock. I slice through the waves and grab onto his white surfboard.

"Can you get back to shore?" I ask.

"The windsurfer belongs to my buddy. It's my first time. I don't know how." His voice trembles. Is it from the cold?

The windsurfer looks around eighteen. I take a quick glance at his tanned muscles and sandy, blond hair. He seems vulnerable and afraid. His blue eyes narrow. "Now what?" he asks.

I reach into the cockpit and take out a rope. "Hold on." I toss the rope. He misses. I throw it again and he catches it. "Paddle to my stern[4] with your hands." His board moves directly behind me. "Tie the other end through that yellow loop." I point.

He fumbles for what seems like several painful minutes. "Got it."

I stroke hard, straining to move us.

"Hit it," the boy calls.

"What?"

"That's what you shout, in water skiing, when you're ready to take off."

I smile. Slowly, we make our way. My paddle dips into the water, first to the right, then to the left. Beads of sweat form on my forehead.

---

3 **windsurfer:** a term that refers both to a sailboard and to a person who uses one

4 **stern:** the rear end of a boat

Suddenly, I surge ahead. I turn around. "You let go." I circle and give him back the rope. "Wrap it around your wrist."

"Sorry."

"It's okay. What's your name?"

"Jamie." His teeth chatter. The water churns around his board. He is soaked. I don't like the blue colour of his lips.

"I'm Teresa. Don't worry, Jamie. It will be slow because we're going against the current. I promise to get you back in one piece." It takes too much energy to talk. Instead, I get him chatting. "Tell me about yourself."

"I thought I was good at all water sports, but windsurfing sure isn't one of them," he laughs.

I don't mean to answer. It just comes out. "Maybe with practice."

"Dumb to go out so far. I don't know what I'm doing." He changes the rope to the other hand, flexing the stiff one.

The wind changes. A big wave hits Jamie sideways, knocking him into the dark, chilly water. He shoots to the top for air and tangles in my slack rescue rope.

He is trapped underneath the sail.

"Jamie!" I scream. The wind swallows my voice. Quickly, I position my boat perpendicular to his board, like a *T.* I drop my paddle, grabbing the tip of his sail at the mast. I tug. Nothing. The water on top of the sail makes it heavy. I drop it. I try again. One, two, three, heave. I grunt, as I break the air pocket and lift the sail a couple of inches. It's enough to let Jamie wriggle out. He explodes to the surface, gulping in air. He pulls himself safely onto the surfboard. I reach over to help untangle the rope from around his foot. I can see an ugly rope burn.

My kayak starts to tip. I throw my weight to the opposite side to keep from flipping. My heart beats fast. "Keep hold of the rope."

"Got it."

"Where's my paddle?" My throat tightens. I search the water. "There it is," I sigh with relief. It's floating a few feet away. My hands pull through the water, acting like paddles. I reach out and grab the shaft of my paddle.

"Hang on, Jamie." The waves swell. The current changes and we ride the waves like a bucking bronco.

I have to keep away from shore or the waves will crash us against the granite, splitting us in half. Just as we clear the rocks, a cross-current hits me. My kayak flips. I'm sitting upside down in the water. *Don't panic.*

Do the Eskimo roll.[5] I get my paddle in the ready position. Then I swing the blade away from the boat's side. I arch my back around and through, keeping my head low. I sweep my blade through the water, pulling hard. I right the kayak and gasp for breath.

"You gave me a heart attack." Jamie looks white.

"Caught me by surprise." We drift, while I catch my breath. The clouds turn black. The water becomes dead calm. "For now, it will be easy going. It's going to storm any minute." I paddle fast and hard. The rain comes down in buckets.

"I'm already wet, so it doesn't matter," Jamie jokes.

I like his sense of humor, but I'm not used to talking to a guy. I've never had a boyfriend. Who would be interested in me?

"You don't know what it's like being so helpless," Jamie says.

I bite my lip. The kayak drifts. I see my parents waving from shore.

My father runs into the water to help. Everything happens real fast. He takes control. Before I know it, Jamie and I are safely back. My mother runs over with towels. Jamie wraps the towel around himself and pulls the windsurfer onto the sand. I stay in my kayak. Half the kayak is on land. The rest is in the water. I feel trapped, like a beached whale.

A turkey vulture circles above me, decides I'm not dead and flies away. I feel dead inside.

Jamie comes back and stands over me. "Do you need help?" he asks.

I shake my head, no. *Go away!* I scream in my head. *Go away, everybody!*

"Thanks for saving my skin," Jamie says.

"Next time, wear a life jacket."

Jamie doesn't flinch. "You're right. That was dumb." It is pouring even harder. Jamie hugs the wet towel around him. "Aren't you getting out?" he asks.

"Yes." Tears sting my eyes, mixed with the rain. My mother pushes a wheelchair over. My father lifts me. A blanket is wrapped around my shivering shoulders. I motion for my parents to leave me alone. Surprised, they move away, but stay close by. Jamie stares.

"Say something." My voice quivers. A fat bullfrog croaks and jumps into the water. I want to jump in after him and swim away somewhere safe. I say nothing more.

---

5 **Eskimo roll:** a technique used for righting an overturned kayak

"Teresa," he clears his throat. "I didn't know."

I watch his discomfort. I've seen it all before. Awkwardness. Forced conversation. A feeble excuse and a fast getaway. My closer friends tried a little harder. They lasted two or three visits. Then, they stopped coming around.

The silence drags on. A mosquito buzzes around my head. So annoying. Why can't they both leave? It lands on my arm and I smack it.

"Do you like roasting marshmallows?" asks Jamie.

"Huh?"

"I like mine burnt to a crisp."

I hate small talk. My hands turn white, as I clutch the armrests of my wheelchair. "What you really want to know is how long I've been crippled."

Jamie winces. He doesn't say anything. I wish he would leave. The air feels heavy and suffocating. I decide to make it easy for him. I'll go first. I push on the wheels with my hands. The sand is wet. The wheels bury, instead of thrusting the wheelchair forward. I stop pushing. Another helpless moment. My parents are watching, waiting for my signal to look after me.

Jamie puts his hand on my shoulder. "Would you like to join me and my friends at a campfire tonight?"

"I don't need pity," I retort.

Jamie smiles. "Actually, I need a date. Everybody is a couple, except me. Where's your campsite?"

"Granite Saddle number 1026." *Why do I tell him? What's the matter with me?* I stare at my wheelchair and then at my kayak. My eyes water. Through tears, I see two images of me: the helpless child on land and the independent woman on water. I blink and the land and water merge. I become one.

I smile back at him.

Jamie pushes me past my parents. They stare at me, in confusion. "It's okay. I'll take Teresa to your campsite." My parents walk behind at a safe distance, moving slowly, despite the rain. We stop at my tent. I smell the fragrance of wet pine needles.

"I'll pick you up at nine." An ember flickers in the wet fireplace, catching our eyes. Sparks rise up into the sky. Jamie takes my hand. "One other thing."

"Yes?" I choke out.

"Bring the marshmallows." ❧

Meeting the Demons

DAWNA MARKOVA

Once upon a time, a long time ago, and very far from here, a great Tibetan poet named Milarepa studied and meditated for decades. He traveled the countryside, teaching the practice of compassion and mercy to the villagers he met. He faced many hardships, difficulties, and sorrows, and transformed them into the path of his awakening.

Finally, it was time to return to the small hut he called home. He had carried its memory in his heart through all the years of his journey. Much to his surprise, upon entering he found it filled with enemies of every kind. Terrifying, horrifying, monstrous demons that would make most people run. But Milarepa was not most people.

Inhaling and exhaling slowly three times, he
turned towards the demons, fully
present and aware. He looked deeply into
the eyes of each, bowing in respect,
and said, "You are here in my home now. I
honor you, and open myself to what
you have to teach me."

As soon as he uttered these words, all of the
enemies save five disappeared. The ones
that remained were grisly, raw, huge
monsters. Milarepa bowed once more and
began to sing a song to them, a sweet melody
resonant with caring for the ways these
beasts had suffered, and curiosity about
what they needed and how he could help
them. As the last notes left his lips,
four of the demons disappeared into
thin air.

Now only one nasty creature was left, fangs
dripping evil, nostrils flaming, opened
jaws revealing a dark, foul black throat.
Milarepa stepped closer to this huge demon,
breathed deeply into his own belly, and
said with quiet compassion, "I must under-
stand your pain and what it is you
need in order to be healed." Then he put
his head in the mouth of this enemy.

In that instant, the demon disappeared
and Milarepa was home at last. ❧

RESPONDING TO CLUSTER FOUR

ESSENTIAL QUESTION: WHAT IS THE VALUE OF FRIENDSHIP?

Thinking Skill SYNTHESIZING

The last selections in this book provide an opportunity for independent learning and the application of the critical thinking skill, synthesis. *Synthesizing* means examining all the things you have learned from this book and combining them to form a richer and more meaningful view of the value of friendship.

There are many ways to demonstrate what you know about friendship. Here are some possibilities. Your teacher may provide others.

1. Break into small groups, with each group taking responsibility for teaching a part of the final cluster. To teach the lesson you might:

   a) create discussion questions and lead a discussion

   b) develop vocabulary activities

   c) prepare a test for the cluster selections

   As you develop your activity, keep the essential question in mind: "What is the value of friendship?"

2. Based on what you have read and your own experience, explain how a friend can become an enemy or an enemy become a friend. Provide examples to support your ideas.

3. Individually or in small groups, develop an independent project that demonstrates your feelings about friendship. For example, you might give a presentation on how to keep a friend or on how not to lose one. Other options might include a music video, dance, poem, performance, drama, or artistic rendering.

Acknowledgments

Text Credits CONTINUED FROM PAGE 2   "Dirk the Protector" from *My Life In Dog Years* by Gary Paulsen. Copyright © 1998 by Gary Paulsen. Used by permission of Delacorte Press, a division of Random House, Inc.

"Farewell, My Friend." Taken from the Roger Ebert Column by Roger Ebert. Copyright © 1999. Dist. by UNIVERSAL PRESS SYNDICATE. Reprinted with permission. All rights reserved.

"For Friendship" from *The Collected Poems of Robert Creeley 1945-1975*. Copyright © 1983 by Robert Creeley. Reprinted with the permission of the University of California Press.

"For Heidi With Blue Hair," copyright © Fleur Adcock 1986. Reprinted from *The Incident Book* by Fleur Adcock (1986) by permission of Oxford University Press.

"Hey, Jealousy" by Francesca Delbanco, from *Seventeen*, December 1997. Copyright © 1997. Distributed by the Los Angeles Times Syndicate. Reprinted by permission.

"Joe King" from *Mama Makes Up Her Mind and Other Dangers of Southern Living* by Bailey White. Copyright © 1993 by Bailey White. Reprinted by permission of Perseus Books Publishers, a member of Perseus Books, L. L. C.

"Jones and the Stray" by Martha Soukup, from *A Starfarer's Dozen: Stories of Things To Come* edited by Michael Stearns. Copyright © 1995 by Martha Soukup. Reprinted by permission of the author.

"The Kayak" by Debbie Spring, from *Takes: Stories for Young Adults* (Thistledown Press, 1996). Reprinted with permission of Thistledown Press.

"Meeting the Demons" excerpted from *No Enemies Within* by Dawna Markova, copyright © 1994 by Dawna Markova, used by permission of Conari Press.

"Moco Limping" by David Nava Monreal. From *Sighs & Songs of Aztlán*, F. E. Albi, Ed., copyright © 1978. Reprinted by permission of F. E. Albi.

"Promises" by Ellen Conford from *Birthday Surprises: Ten Great Stories to Unwrap*, edited by Johanna Hurwitz. Text copyright © 1995 by Ellen Conford. Compilation copyright © 1995 by Morrow Junior Books. By permission of Morrow Junior Books, a division of William Morrow and Company, Inc.

"Scream of the Little Bird" by David S. Jackson/Cordova from *Time*, December 14, 1998. Copyright © 1998 Time Inc. Reprinted by permission.

"Shaking" from *Sigodlin* by Robert Morgan. Copyright © 1990 by Robert Morgan, Wesleyan University Press by permission of University Press of New England.

"Take Your Best Shot" from *A Trick of the Light* by Jackie Vivelo. Copyright © 1987 by Jacqueline J. Vivelo. Reprinted by permission of the author.

"War Game" by Nancy Werlin, copyright © 1997 by Nancy Werlin. From *Twelve Shots: Outstanding Short Stories About Guns* edited by Harry Mazer. Used by permission of Dell Publishing, a division of Random House, Inc.

Every reasonable effort has been made to properly acknowledge ownership of all material used. Any omissions or mistakes are not intentional and, if brought to the publisher's attention, will be corrected in future editions.

Photo and Art Credits   Cover: George Giusti. *Civilization is a method of living, an attitude of equal respect for all men,* 1955. National Museum of American Art, Washingtin, DC/Art Resource, NY. Page 3, 4-5: Roy Gumpel/©Tony Stone Images. Page 9: Super Stock. Page 10, 11: Jerry Ohlinger's Movie Materials. Page 13: Index Stock Imagery. Page 14: ©Edward Holub/Phototonica. Pages 20-21: ©Charles Register/Picturesque Stock Photo. Page 23: Tony Garcia/©Tony Stone Images. Page 27: Lucien Freud, *A Filly,* 1969. Mixed media. 34.5 x 24cm. Courtesy Mathew Marks Gallery, NY. Page 28: Photograph by Michael Nye, published in *What Have You Lost?* edited by Naomi Shihab Nye, Greenwillow Press. This photograph is part of a permanent public arts installation, *No Age is Empty,* at the University Family Health Center Southeast, San Antonio, TX. Page 45: Duane Michals, *Now Becoming Then.* Page 47: John P. Kelly/Image Bank. Page 48, 55. Katherine Dunn. Page 56: John Nieto, *God's Dog Wolf,* Acrylic 30 x 24. Courtesy of the artist. Page 68: ©1999 Jeff Schultz/Alaska Stock Images. Page 71: © Jonathan Safir/Photonica. Page. 76: ©Superstock. Page. 83: Duane Michals, *Chance Meeting* (from a series). Pages. 84-85: William Burlingham. Page 86: ©1992 Jacob Taposchaner/FPG International. Pages\ 98–99: Bibliothèque nationale de France. Pages 102-103: (Detail) *Childe Wynd and the Laidley Worm* from a Victorian painting on display at Bambergh Castle. Photo courtesy Marc Alexander. Page: ©Superstock. Page 104: ©Mitsuru Yamaguchi/Photonica. Page 111: ©1995 Buena Vista Television. Page 113: Sergio Ortiz/West Stock. Page 114: ©1968 Bruce Davidson/Magnum Photos. Inc. Page 125: ©Chris Warren/International Stock. Pages 126-127: Michael Levins, *Untitled (From the 3rd Avenue El, NY.),* 1970. Museum of Fine Arts Boston. Pages 128, 135: Mary Jones. Page 136: Paul Harris/©Tony Stone Images. Pages 141, 142. William J. Hebert/©Tony Stone Images.